D1610162

CAMPS ON CRIME

CAMPS ON CRIME

Francis E. Camps

Formerly Professor of Forensic Medicine
University of London

With a preface by
Professor Sir Leon Radzinowicz

David & Charles : Newton Abbot

0 7153 5941 X

Set in 11/13-point Plantin
and printed in Great Britain
by W J Holman Limited Dawlish
for David & Charles (Holdings) Limited
South Devon House Newton Abbot Devon

Contents

List of Illustrations

PLATES

LINE IN TEXT

Preface

by
Professor Sir Leon Radzinowicz

ONE evening, fourteen years ago, Francis Camps visited our home for the first time. I have never, before or since, seen my wife evince so sustained an interest in criminology. He talked to us about investigations in which he had personally taken a part: the fascinating technical aspects; the modus operandi of murderers; the minutiae of their trials. But he was more than a forensic stamp collector, attracted by the rare and bizarre for its own sake. He was constantly opening out broader vistas, more humane perspectives, questions of moral guilt and innocence, and of the differing shades of guilt where guilt there was. His was a subtle mind, not given to writing off either people or actions in terms of black and white. And this was all the more impressive because he was a man of action and such men are not always blessed with that kind of insight.

The essays that make up this book put on permanent record something of his rare and stimulating outlook, his vivid and varied experience. Their subjects need no introduction from me. They are famous cases, in their time gravely deliberated in our courts, still full of fascination. Professor Camps recounts them in a simple, straightforward way, with the sure touch which only a master and a craftsman could hope to achieve. Some are his own cases; some belong to the more distant past but are still of great importance in medical jurisprudence; some, like the story of Jack the Ripper, remain mysteries beyond solution.

Francis Camps sums up his fundamental philosophy of investigation as hard work, attention to detail and emotional detachment. All these he brought in full measure to his forensic work. But he brought much more. His vocation was far broader than that of mere medical detective. He was as interested in proceeding by way of the highest standards of justice as in bringing crimes home to their perpetrators and assessing guilt. He had an acute perception of what criminal justice should be in a civilised country. No reform was too modest, too pedestrian, to receive his attention if it would contribute to that great end. There are dozens of such measures promoted in his books, his lectures and, above all, in the minds of his many collaborators, old and young.

The British Academy of Forensic Sciences sprang from his profound conviction that reforms in criminal justice could not be imposed from above by a *deus ex machina*, but must be achieved by intense collective effort, sustained over many years. He had faith in expertise, but not hidden within four walls, imposed willy-nilly upon ignorant masses. It had to be made public, the open expertise of a democratic society, in which changes can be achieved only with general understanding and support.

The Academy, going from strength to strength and publishing its own influential Journal, is one of his monuments. Another is his department at The London Hospital Medical College, which he built up into a leading centre. That also will go on developing, since it is manned by people he imbued with his own enthusiasm and sense of duty. And then there are all the good deeds he has left behind him around the world through his visits, his lectures, his advice, support and encouragement to struggling causes and pioneers. He knew how to make a scheme a reality and how to do it quickly. He knew how to involve others and to kindle enthusiasm in them. He understood the needs and approaches of people from widely divergent backgrounds.

It is a sad privilege to be asked to write this preface, which must also in a sense be an obituary. Yet I cannot, in honesty, say I wish it had been offered to another. It gives me a last opportunity to pay tribute to a distinguished and most lovable man.

University of Cambridge
January 1973

Introduction

ALTHOUGH a relatively new discipline, criminology is now recognised as a formidable science. The man who has probably done most to establish its credentials in Britain is Sir Leon Radzinowicz of the Institute of Criminology at Cambridge University.

I myself have been involved in criminology—most especially, pathology—since 1935, the year I was appointed county pathologist of Essex. When my friend Jonathan Goodman suggested that a selection of the papers I have presented to a wide variety of audiences should be published as a book, I readily agreed, for I saw this as an opportunity to show the changing face of the subject. It would allow me to illustrate the tremendous advances that have been made in recent decades, while at the same time demonstrating that there has been little, if any, change in the fundamental philosophy of investigation, which can be summed up in three phrases: hard work, attention to detail, and lack of emotional involvement. Criminology must be a subject of integrity. I have no shame in admitting mistakes, for this is the honourable approach and allows the science to gain greater strength.

A friend and personal adviser questioned the inclusion in this book of the subject of drug addiction, but this is a basically new problem which is, as yet, unsolved in the United States of America, where it is perhaps most acute. Although the Bonnyman case involves the therapeutic drug addict, it is one of the first convictions for manslaughter involving drugs.

The historical case of poisoning with cherry laurel water (cyanide) shows how not to be blinded by science, and could well be the present-day yardstick for the scrutiny of scientific evidence.

The Jack the Ripper case is a perfect example of how not to investigate. At the same time it shows how easy it is for the amateur sleuth or over-enthusiastic journalist to build up a case against an individual—especially if he has insufficient data. It is essential not to dismiss lightly the pleas of a person who claims to be innocent. Because the public blindly accept a conviction as proof of guilt does not mean that a man in prison, who proclaims that he is innocent and that force of circumstance led to his conviction, should be disregarded. Proof of motivation for a crime often plays a large part in the verdict of a jury—but a motive does not necessarily mean an act.

A great deal of emphasis has been, and still is, placed on pathologists; this is mainly due to the influence and unintended celebrity of the late Sir Bernard Spilsbury. Forensic medicine has been the real contributor to criminology, and this is as it should be, for a knowledge of medicine and the workings of the human being should play a prominent part, not only in the investigation of crimes of violence, but also in arriving at a verdict and in disposing of a convicted person—*res ipsa loquiter.*

F.E.C.

1 Crime in Hunter's Time

JOHN HUNTER (1728-93) is renowned as one of the founders of modern surgery. His boundless energy and curiosity in all scientific fields led to an unrivalled breadth of knowledge and interests. A tireless research worker as well as a brilliant innovative surgeon, he established the principles of surgery on a sound biological foundation. His reputation is enshrined in the Hunterian Society, which has a remarkable collection of his writings and possessions, and also in the Hunterian Museum at the Royal College of Surgeons.

The case of cyanide poisoning described in the following paper illustrates Hunter's adherence to scientific method and his refusal to be cajoled into unjustified conclusions based on incomplete experimentation.

Originally I conceived the idea of discussing the similarity between the medico-legal problems of the period of John Hunter and the present day. Indeed, Foderé, in the introduction to his treatise on Legal Medicine, describes the eighteenth century as 'an era remarkable for the conversion of the human mind from the enthusiasm of poetry and the fine arts to the cultivation and study of the exact sciences', whilst the last fifty years could equally well be notable as a period remarkable for the greater advancement of scientific knowledge of the exact sciences. This is of

considerable significance for, to quote Foderé again, 'It is necessary to convey that ignorance and, even more particularly, "demi-
science" lends more often to false or uncertain appearance of the
truth and of evidence.'

Whilst examining the literature, it has become more and more
evident not only how closely the philosophy of Hunter was
applicable to the problems of his time but how well his challenge
to 'work out theories' could be applied to those of the present day.
His name and his ideas were so frequently intruding themselves
into the different matters which came to my notice that, as a
result, the only important medico-legal case in which he himself
played an active part became essential as part of this paper.

In order to understand the problems and practice of legal
medicine in England and Scotland in the eighteenth century, it is
necessary to appreciate that, whereas on the Continent of Europe
—and especially in Austria, Germany and France—it was a
recognised speciality with professorial chairs in State or Forensic
Medicine, the first chair to be established in the British Isles was
in Edinburgh as late as 1807. It is not surprising, therefore, that
publications on medico-legal subjects, although no novelty on the
Continent, were relatively rare here. On the other hand, anatomy
and physiology were developing sciences, and it was to be expected that anatomists and surgeons would appear as expert witnesses in such cases which were of sufficient importance to appear
in the records. It is of interest that, of the few English medico-
legal papers of significance, that of William Hunter on Infanticide
(1783), entitled 'The Uncertainty of the Signs of Murder in the
Case of Bastard Children', was commended by Foderé in his
'Traité de Medecine Légale et d'Hygiène Publique' (1813). John
Hunter's own contributions of medico-legal interest included an
essay on 'Post-mortem digestion of the stomach' (1772) and on
'The recovery of people apparently drowned' (1776), and, as he
said in evidence in the Donellan case (1781), he carried out large
numbers of animal experiments of toxicological importance. It is,
however, of much greater interest that he noted that coagulation

of the blood did not take place in animals killed by lightning, by violent blows in the stomach or by exhaustion by hunting, and thereby anticipated fibrinolysis, a technique which was of extreme medico-legal importance in two modern cases: R. v Ruxton (1935) and R. v Hume (1949), both of which were associated with dismemberment after death.

The influence that Hunter himself has—or could have exerted —on modern legal medicine will be mentioned later but it would now appear to be an opportune moment to draw attention to the similarity between a problem of medical teaching in Hunter's day and two contemporary situations of extreme importance. I refer to the inadequate supply of human cadavers for anatomical dissection in the eighteenth century and the short supply of experimental animals and of human tissues for transplantation at the present time. All these situations have arisen from the laws of supply and demand. The demand in all three circumstances must be attributed to almost explosive scientific advances but, whereas in the second half of the eighteenth century it was due to the new techniques of injection and preservation for anatomical dissection, in recent years experimental pathology and surgery and the stricter control of testing of new drugs are probably the main causes. The short supply of anatomical specimens involved the curious position that if a proper knowledge of practical anatomy was to be enforced, as envisaged by legislation for medical students, then the means of achieving this would render them liable to disgrace and punishment. In this respect, the law resembled that of Venice as interpreted by Portia, that in exacting the pound of flesh, it forbade the operation necessary for its removal. Thus, although the penalties for 'illegal exhumation' were (if detected) strongly enforced (there were fourteen convictions in England in one year) by fines, imprisonment and even transportation, such penalties did not interfere with the equally inexorable laws of supply and demand. In fact, not only was the trade local but brisk exports from London led to the Leith smack sometimes including in her cargo as many as twelve bodies. From this

B

it was not a far call to murder to provide a body in periods of shortage, especially if adequate remuneration was available. However, the members of the public whose relatives were the object of these operations responded somewhat violently and publicly. The result was that, ultimately, in 1832, the Anatomy Act was passed which regulated the legal position of anatomists and, *inter alia*, abolished the dissection of bodies of murderers and felons who had, in the past, been the main source of supply.

The position at present with regard to the supply of experimental animals is that the demand has increased and the cost of bred animals is high—especially with the limited money available. This not unnaturally means that any other supply, such as from dealers, becomes suspect and may be emotionally linked with the possibility of 'stolen pets' labelled as 'strays'.

The other problem which has arisen is due to scientific advances connected with the transplantation of human tissues, a true Hunterian association. In this connection, the Anatomy Act which limited the dissection (post-mortem examination) of any body to anatomists except when ordered by a legal authority (the Coroner) theoretically debarred autopsies from being carried out by pathologists, even with the relatives' consent. This situation has now been altered by the Human Tissue Act (1961) which allows tissues to be removed by a registered medical practitioner who has pronounced life extinct. Unfortunately, there is no true definition of death, a shortcoming to which attention was drawn in the Potter case (1963) and which has led the Church Assembly Board for Social Responsibility (1965) to consider once again the quotation made by Osler from Arthur Hugh Clough:

> *'Thou shalt not kill; but needst not strive*
> *officiously to keep alive.'*

It is when faced with the definition of death, a situation that was not even contemplated 50 years ago, that the contribution of John Hunter to the philosophy of modern legal medicine must be appreciated. His skill and care in dissection, his breadth of interests, his integrity in the witness box and his approach, so well typified by the quotation 'I think your solution is just; but why think? Why not try the experiment?', might well have avoided the period of dogma and adherence to 'worn out' theories which have stood in the way of the speciality achieving its full and proper status.

An example of how his approach to a problem can produce valuable information was in the case of the death of Sergeant Watters (R. v. Emmett Dunne, 1955), who was found hanging in the barracks at Duisberg, Germany, in 1953. At the time it was assumed that he had committed suicide but, because of subsequent rumours, his body was exhumed a year later. The injuries carefully described by an Army pathologist who performed the original autopsy were confirmed and help was obtained from photographs taken at the same time, which provided data which enabled the following three questions to be answered:

(1) Had the body been hanged after death? and, if so, would the tongue protrude between the teeth?
(2) What would cause a vertical fracture of the thyroid cartilage?
(3) Why were there vertical tears in the intima of both carotid arteries?

(1) Without going into details, it was possible to show, by using material available under the Anatomy Act, that the marks on the neck could have been caused by the cord being applied after death. Also, provided that rigor mortis had not set in before a body was suspended by the neck after death, the pressure of the cord would cause the tongue to protrude, which would mean that with the onset of rigor mortis, it would be gripped between the teeth.

(2) The fracture of the larynx could be produced by a blow with a hard smooth linear object, delivered across the front of the neck. Initially the possibility of a ju-jitsu blow was considered to be a possibility and a demonstration was arranged with a Japanese expert. This showed that, although adequate force could be applied by the edge of the hand, the position and direction of the

classical ju-jitsu blow would be wrong. At the same time an unarmed combat blow would produce such an injury.

(3) When the carotid artery is full at normal blood pressure, a
transverse (crush) blow will produce vertical tears in the intima.
All these observations were later confirmed by eye-witness
evidence and the admission of the accused man.

It is fortunate for our study that Hunter appeared as an expert
in one of the most celebrated criminal cases of the century and
that a full transcript of the evidence is available. Withaus'
Manual of Toxicology (1911) has called it the earliest English
trial for murder by cyanic poisons (laurel water). It draws attention to Paris and Fonblanque (1823) wherein a part of the evidence is reproduced. The following is a report of

The Trial of John Donellan, Esq.
for the Wilful Murder of
Sir Theodosius Edward Allesley Boughton, Bart,
at the Assize at Warwick, on Friday, March 30th, 1781.

Summary of the Indictment:

That John Donellan did put in, or infuse in two drachms of
arsenic and mix together with water and put into a glass phial
bottle value one penny, and did place it instead of medicine prescribed and made up, intending Sir Theodosius to take it by
mistaking the same for the medicine. That Sir Theodosius did
swallow the arsenic believing it to be the medicine and as a result
became sick and did die.

That the said John Donellan by means aforesaid did feloniously
and wilfully and of malice aforethought poison, kill and murder
Sir Theodosius Boughton against the peace of our Sovereign
Lord the King.

This Indictment was found by the Grand Inquest a True Bill.
The prisoner, upon his arraignment, pleaded Not Guilty whereupon a petit jury were sworn and charged with the prisoner and
the trial commenced at 7.30 a.m. before the Honourable Francis
Buller, Esq, one of the Justices of His Majesty's Court of King's
Bench, and was taken down in shorthand by Joseph Gurney,
upon whose transcript this report is based.

For the Crown were Mr Howorth, Mr Wheeler and others,

whilst for the Defence were Mr Newnham, Mr Green and others.

The facts of the case were outlined by Mr Howorth, who led for the Prosecution, in his opening speech. His introduction is a remarkable description of homicidal poisoning.

The offence is easy of penetration but difficulty of detection. The murderer by poison is not pointed out to justice by the bloody marks of his guilt or the fatal instrument of his crime; his horrid purpose is planned in secret, is executed without his presence; his guilt can only be traced by circumstances but circumstances sometimes do, and in this case I trust, will, as plainly reveal the guilty hand, as if an hundred witnesses testified the actual commission of the crime.

The following is a convenient summary of the case for the Prosecution, taken from this speech.

Sir Theodosius Boughton, a young man of an ancient and respectable family would have, had he attained the age of 21, inherited an opulent fortune, but should he die before, it would go to his sister, Mrs Donellan, the wife of the accused. The evidence will show that for a short time before his death, the accused had on several occasions expressed the opinion that Boughton was in a poor state of health and that his life was 'not worth one year's purchase'. Sir Theodosius was intending to go and stay with a young friend in Northamptonshire until he came of age, and this, it is suggested, called for immediate action if the accused was to lay his hands on the family fortune. At the time, Sir Theodosius was being attended by a Mr Powell, an apothecary, who was treating him for a 'slight venereal disorder' he had contracted and was giving him 'some cooling medicines'. On Tuesday, 29th August, Mr. Powell made up a harmless draught and sent it by a servant in the evening to Sir Theodosius to be taken on the Wednesday morning.

On the same evening Sir Theodosius, accompanied by most of the servants, went fishing. Lady Boughton and Mrs. Donellan were, in the meantime, walking in the garden for some hours. The exact whereabouts of Mr. Donellan is not known except that when he joined the ladies at 7 p.m. he told them that he had been fishing with Sir Theodosius and was worried that he might catch cold if he stayed late by the river (it was proved that he had not joined Sir Theodosius at all).

When Sir Theodosius returned home he was in perfect health —ate his supper and went to bed. The following morning he does not appear to have been ill for he 'leapt out of bed' according to his servant.

At about seven o'clock his mother, Lady Boughton, got up and went into Sir Theodosius' room to give him his medicine. He asked her to reach down the draught which was standing on a shelf in his bedroom (it was alleged the medicine had, at one time, been locked up but, on the advice of the accused, this had been discontinued). After taking it from the shelf, Lady Boughton poured it into a cup and gave it to her son who, when he had swallowed only half of it, complained that it was 'nauseous to the taste'—'disagreeable to smell' and that he did not think he 'could keep it down'. Lady Boughton thought it had a peculiar smell which suggested to her the smell of bitter almonds! In spite of this she again gave him the cup and he swallowed the rest, asking for a bit of cheese to chew to take away the taste. She also gave him a little water which, after washing out his mouth, he spat out and laid himself down. After a few minutes he appeared to be in agony, his stomach heaved and his eyes appeared to be affected. This Lady Boughton attributed to the draught having upset his stomach and an attempt not to be sick. A few minutes later, when he had become more composed, she left the room thinking he was going to sleep but, on her return after about ten minutes, she found him seriously ill with 'fixed pupils'—'clenched teeth' —'heaving stomach' and 'foaming at the mouth'. He died half an hour later and Lady Boughton will say that whatever the draught, it was not his usual one because it had a different smell.

Experiments made by learned and intelligent men showed that the medicine was laurel water. What is more significant: the accused was skilled in distillation and possessed a still, which he produced, filled with lime, about two weeks after the death. The reason he gave for its contents was that he had done this to 'put under his bed to kill fleas'!

Lady Boughton, astonished by her son's death, sent for Captain Donellan and for Mr. Powell, the apothecary. On his arrival, the accused behaved in a somewhat extraordinary manner when told by Lady Boughton that she thought the medicine was wrong for he took up the bottle, poured water into it and shook it and threw the contents into a basin of dirty water. In spite of Lady Boughton's remonstration that everything should remain as it was, he picked up a second bottle, added water, took it on his finger and treated it in the same way. Then, when a maidservant came into the room, he insisted on her taking away the bottles, and dirty things, and cleaning the room; all this in spite of protests by Lady Boughton, and at a time when it was by no means clear that death had taken place.

On the arrival of Mr. Powell, the accused, instead of asking about the medicine he had sent and telling him about the effect it appeared to have had, told him that Sir Theodosius must have caught cold fishing. In fact, Mr. Powell was actually allowed to leave the house without knowing anything about the medicine. In the meantime, Captain Donellan occupied his time telling everybody that Sir Theodosius must have caught cold when he got his feet wet fishing (how he knew this is not clear, as he was not there). This was contradicted by Lady Boughton who had noticed that his stockings were not damp. He also sent a letter to Sir William Wheeler, the dead man's guardian, as follows: —

'I am sorry to be the communicator of Sir Theodosius' death to you; he has for some time past been under the care of Mr. Powell of Rugby for a similar complaint to that which he had at Eton.'

This impressed upon Sir William's mind that the death was due to natural disease and, as a result, no enquiry was set on foot whilst the body remained in the house until Saturday and, in fact, was put in a coffin. [No death certificate was necessary. Births & Deaths Reg. 1874.] However, rumours had started elsewhere by reason of the manner of the young man's death and eventually reached the ears of Sir William who wrote on Monday to the accused saying that death must have been due to poison and therefore, in order to satisfy the family, the body must be 'opened', at the same time naming the persons he wished to do the examination: Dr. Rattray, Mr. Wilmer and Mr. Snow. Captain Donellan duly sent for them and also wrote to Sir William, agreeing that the body should be opened and Sir William replied saying that he was glad that this was being done. At 8 p.m. Dr. Rattray and Mr. Wilmer arrived at Lawford Hall and were met by the accused who, after he was told they had not heard from Sir William, showed them the envelope of the first letter (containing the suspicion of poisoning and request that the body be opened) and the contents of the second letter, in which Sir William expressed satisfaction that the family had agreed.

Also, on their enquiry as to why they had been sent for to open the body, he said 'for the satisfaction of us all' and made no mention that it was to allay suspicions and establish the cause of death. It was not surprising therefore that, when shown a body in an advanced state of putrefaction, they declined to do anything and were sent away, still without asking them the cause of death. On the following morning a surgeon, Mr. Bucknill, called and expressed the firm intention of opening the body in order to give satisfaction to the public. This he was not permitted to do.

On 5th September, Captain Donellan wrote to Sir William Wheeler:

'Dear Sir,

Give me leave to express the heartfelt satisfaction I enjoyed in the receipt of your letter, as it gave Lady Boughton, my wife, and self the opportunity of instantly observing your advice in all respects. I sent for Dr. Rattray and Dr. Wilmer and they brought another gentleman with them; Mr. Powell gave them the meeting and upon receipt of your last letter, I gave it them to peruse and act as is directed. The four gentlemen proceeded accordingly and I am happy to inform you that they fully satisfied us.'

This letter also satisfied Sir William but only until 3 or 4 days later when he had learned that the body had not been opened and immediately demanded that Mr. Bucknill and Mr. Snow be sent for. When Mr. Bucknill arrived, Mr. Snow was not yet there and Mr. Bucknill went off to see a patient. Mr. Snow then arrived and was told that Mr. Wilmer had declined to open the body due to putrefaction and therefore went away. Mr. Bucknill then came back and was told the reason for Mr. Snow's departure and also left. Still the body was unopened. The body was buried on that day, after a letter had been dispatched to Sir William, enquiring whether he wanted the funeral to be postponed.

However, the circumstances of it being buried without being 'opened' caused 'wonderful alarm' and there was a demand that the Coroner be informed which resulted in the body being 'taken up' and 'opened'. At the Coroner's enquiry (Inquest) when Lady Boughton was telling about Captain Donellan having washed out the bottles, the Captain tried to stop her evidence by 'pulling on her sleeve'. On the third day of the Inquest, the Captain wrote to the Coroner and Jury that he recollected that Sir Theodosius had procured things to kill rats, including 'arsenic by the pound weight' and that he 'laid' it all over the house in spite of remonstrations as to its danger.

In spite of this plausible explanation, the jury committed him to gaol on a Coroner's warrant and, whilst there, he made communications to various people and also wrote a letter to his wife. This he sent unsealed and wrote 'that you do longer remain where you are likely to undergo the fate of those that have gone already by sudden means', a further elaboration which may well have influenced the result of his trial.

At this stage, before introducing the evidence of John Hunter, a summary of the medical evidence for the Prosecution is essential. Dr Rattray, who said he was a 'physician' at Coventry, dealt with the question of the letters and said that with Mr Wilmer he had gone to the graveyard and there had met Mr Bucknill, Mr Powell and Mr Snow. Mr Bucknill had opened the body—which was in a state of decomposition, swollen and discoloured. He described the organs as being quite obviously decomposed, 'the kidneys appeared as black as tinder', and went on to say that independently of the appearances which indicated poisoning, the draught which had been taken was poison and caused his death. When he was asked to smell a bottle, he identified it as laurel water and also stated that the medicine prepared by Mr Powell was 'innocent and proper'. He testified that he and Mr Wilmer had carried out experiments by administering laurel water. A dog, after forcible administration fell down dead; a mare, after being given $1\frac{1}{2}$ pints, died in 15 minutes, a cat in 3 minutes.

At the beginning of the week he (with Mr Snow) had given another aged horse a pint of laurel water, in repeated doses, and it, too, dropped to the ground. The horse's tongue had 'darted in and out', it had had convulsions and had died in 28 minutes. A post-mortem had shown congestion and that the blood was pink; and, he went on to say, the post mortem appearances of the deceased had confirmed his opinion as far as viewing the body some time after death would do, and that one bottle would be fatal.

Cross-examined, he admitted that the animals' bodies were examined shortly after death. He also said that the condition of the body after exhumation was similar to that when he saw it in the house and agreed that putrefaction had taken place. He admitted that in his report he merely described the bowels and stomach and was asked whether all the findings were due to putrefaction. He agreed that he had examined the stomach, which contained one and a half spoonfuls of blood-stained fluid, and did not pursue his search through the bowels. He had to agree that he thought originally that it was arsenical poisoning but that he had been mistaken and that his opinion was based upon what he had heard from Lady Boughton. He refused to admit that death could have been due to apoplexy or epilepsy because he had never heard of either causing heaving of the stomach. He agreed that forcible administration had made the animal cough. He also said he noticed an 'odd taste' in his mouth at the autopsy and, on this, based his opinion of laurel water poisoning.

Dr Wilmer confirmed the experiments and confirmed what Dr Rattray had said and that the body was putrefied. He also accepted that epilepsy could be due to various causes. Dr Ashe, a physician from Birmingham, said that he thought death was due to poison and that he had heard nothing to lead him to think that the deceased was suffering from any illness. He had to admit that his opinion was based on what he had been told.

Dr Parsons, a Professor of Anatomy from Birmingham, gave as his opinion that death was due to poisoning and not epilepsy or apoplexy. He said convulsions could occur from laurel water. When cross-examined, he said he based his opinion that death was not due to apoplexy on the fact that the dead man was thin. He based his conclusions on the smell of the poison. Mr Bucknill gave no evidence of opening the body. Mr Powell, an apothecary, said that the deceased had swelling of the groin. He produced a phial containing medicine similar to that given to the deceased and said that it contained rhubarb, jalap, spirits of lavender, nutmeg water and simple syrup. On cross-examination he gave the composition as rhubarb and jalap 15 grains, spirits of lavender 20 drops, nutmeg water 2 drachms, simple syrup 2 drachms with $1\frac{1}{2}$oz water. This concluded the case for the Prosecution.

Now we come to the evidence given by John Hunter, for the Defence, reproduced from the original transcript. His examination-in-chief followed the present-day pattern and it is to be noted that Hunter was present in person throughout the trial and that it was upon what he had heard that he based his expert opinion. It is of interest to note his meticulous attention to detail when he corrects, due to a misunderstanding, the impression that he ever saw the dead man, either in life or after death. Later he adopted an attitude that might well be taken today, that the body was too decomposed to allow any reliable opinion to be expressed as to the cause of death ('Cause of death unascertainable'). He then deals with the clinical symptoms and quite properly states that the symptoms are not specific of poisoning and could occur from natural disease. It is of interest to read his frank admission that he has never seen or heard of a case of laurel water poisoning in a human being but gives as his opinion that the effects on animals of a poison are nearly the same as on a human, with the proviso that in the experimental animal they may be due to two things: the forcing of the substance on the animal, such as by aspiration, and the poison itself. Finally he made the telling point that if the skull had been opened and the brain examined, it might have been possible to exclude a cerebral haemorrhage. He ended up with the conclusion that, from the medical evidence, there was no proof of poison on the one hand (no opening or examination of the intestine or chemical examination of its contents) and no disproof that death was due to natural disease on the other.

The cross-examination also followed what might be expected today, and it was put to him whether, when an apparently healthy man swallowed a draught which was followed by certain symptoms and death, it would not be reasonable to conclude that the draught had caused his death? Hunter's answer was that the state of the man's health means nothing for apparently healthy people die suddenly, but he admitted that the circumstances of the draught were suspicious and that it did not require a doctor to infer that. Therefore he correctly declined to usurp the function of the jury.

The slight reprimand he received from the Bench may well have been merited but nevertheless the Judge appears to have accepted Hunter's evidence on the post-mortem examination. At the same time, from his reply Hunter showed his integrity when he admitted that the symptoms after swallowing the draught were in favour of poisoning but would not agree that the draught necessarily caused death. The intervention by the Judge when he asked whether Hunter thought that death so shortly after swallowing the draught did not indicate that it was the cause evoked the somewhat logical answer that if it was proved to be poison, he would agree, but as there was no real proof and it was known that disease could cause the same symptoms and death, then he could not say with certainty.

When challenged as to whether he declined to give an opinion, he replied that he was unable to form any opinion in the absence of any proof of a poison.

He agreed that distilled laurel water could have caused the symptoms but qualified this by saying that from his experiments on animals, death had not been so quick. He had injected laurel into the blood of dogs and they had not died, but had 'thrown it into the stomach' and the effects had not been so rapid; he admitted that it could nevertheless still have produced the symptoms described.

When Counsel for the Defence asked whether apoplexy or epilepsy could have produced similar symptoms without physic, he replied 'Certainly'. An excursion into the question of the likelihood of apoplexy occurring in a young man and whether it was hereditary, led to the suggestion that a thin young man, taking cooling medicines would be unlikely to have an apoplectic seizure. To this he replied that as he did not know the nature of the medicines, he could not say whether they would hinder apoplexy (possibly a hint that he doubted whether such medicines would have any effect).

The final question and answer is reported in full for they show that Hunter refused to be partisan:

Court: Give me your opinion in the best manner you can—one way or the other—whether upon the whole of the symptoms described, the death proceeded from that medicine or any other cause?

Hunter: I do not mean to equivocate but when I tell the sentiments of my mind, what I feel at the time, I can give nothing decisive.

This concluded the evidence for the Defence.

In summing up, after explaining the nature of circumstantial evidence and saying that in cases such as this, evidence must always be circumstantial, the Judge told the jury that they had first to consider whether the deceased died of poison.

For the Prosecution there was evidence by a number of men able in the 'physical' line who had all given as their opinion that death was due to poison. For the Defence 'there is called one gentleman who is likewise of the faculty and a very able man, and I can hardly say what his opinion is for he does not seem to have formed any opinion. He said death could be due to other things. He can say nothing decisive.

'You have, therefore, on one side five positive opinions, on the other no more than doubt, for Mr Hunter agrees that laurel water could have caused the symptoms. If you have doubt about the evidence of the physical gentlemen, then every part of the prisoner's evidence must count.' The Judge then outlined the rest of the evidence.

The jury retired at 6.25 p.m. and returned at 6.34 p.m. with a verdict of 'Guilty'. When sentencing Donellan to death the Judge drew attention to the fact that it was his false accounts which had led to his conviction. The concluding words were: 'and that your body be afterwards delivered to the surgeons to be dissected and anatomised'.

There is recorded in The Annual Register, 1781, on page 172: 'Captain Donellan convicted of the murder of Sir Theodosius Boughton about 7 in the morning was carried in a mourning coach from Warwick gaol to the place of execution and hanged according to his sentence after which the body was given to the surgeons to be dissected.'

Before he was 'turned off', he addressed the spectators on the following lines: 'That as he was going to appear before God to whom all decent was known, he solemnly declared that he was innocent of the crime for which he was to suffer.'

Certain interesting matters arise from the case which are medico-legal, ethical and pharmacological. Examining the case as

a whole, unless someone else substituted a medicine or some
innocent explanation can explain the smell, there can be little
doubt of John Donellan's guilt. His prevarication, alternative
explanations of his brother-in-law's death, removal of the bottles
(reminiscent of Palmer) and attempts to prevent an autopsy,
together with an obvious motive, cannot possibly be countered by
his solicitude for the deceased during the argument in Rugby.
At the same time the medical evidence is not above criticism,
based as it was upon the evidence of Lady Boughton, which can
be summarised as follows. In about two minutes after swallowing
the draught, the deceased appeared to struggle very much as if to
keep it down and had a rattling and gurgling at his stomach. In
about ten minutes he seemed inclined to doze and about five
minutes afterwards he was found with his eyes fixed upwards,
his teeth clenched and froth running from his mouth. He died in
half an hour. She also said the draught, which smelt of bitter
almonds, was described by her son as 'nauseating'.

A short digression into the properties and pharmacology of
laurel water would appear to be justified. Laurel water is made
from a distillation of cherry laurel leaves. The leaves are elliptical,
oblong, four to eight inches in length, stiff and leathery, bright
green and shiny. They have no smell unless bruised, when they
emit an agreeable ratafia odour. The soft part of the leaves con-
tains a glycoside known as prulaurasin; the veins contain an
enzyme known as prunase. When the leaves are crushed, hydrocyanic acid is formed. Fresh leaves yield a volatile oil like that of
bitter almonds. It has been shown that the quantity of oil produced varies with the influence of the seasons on the activity of
the plant. The buds and unexpanded leaves of May and June
contain twice as much as the full sized leaves of July. Twelve-
month-old leaves (May) contain less than a fifth of the June
average. Differences in soil and exposure may affect the oil, and
great care should be taken when seasoning liqueurs and con-
fections.

John Hunter said in evidence that he considered the onset of the symptoms too quick whilst the other experts said that according to their experiments the symptoms would appear that quickly. From hindsight it may well be that both were correct, if consideration is given to the seasonal variation in the strength and other factors.

Alfred Swaine Taylor, in fact, estimates that the amount taken must have been 2-4 grains of pure hydrocyanic acid, the equivalent of 50 drops of Scheele's prussic acid (*Principles and Practice of Medical Jurisprudence,* 1st ed, 1865). My own view is that the early symptoms of nausea and retching may possibly indicate that there was also a gastric irritant such as arsenic, but as no analysis was carried out this must be speculatory. Taylor writes that 'in making every allowance for such coincidences in the supervention of fatal disease at the time of taking medicine or food as have been elsewhere pointed out, I do not think there is any reason to doubt that in this case the deceased was poisoned and the prisoner properly convicted'.

As has already been stated, it is possible to criticise the medical evidence, and it may well be that it was for this reason that Hunter appeared in the case, his whole scientific standard being affronted.

Therefore it is justifiable to examine what the Prosecution witnesses said and how much they contributed to the case.

(1) Dr Rattray initially attributed death to arsenic, but some time later was carrying out experiments with laurel water.

(2) Quite clearly no proper conclusions could be drawn from the autopsy or the earlier reports of appearances, yet all the experts did so.

(3) No attempts were made to obtain information by chemical analysis of the stomach and intestinal contents.

(4) In any event, the intestines were not even opened.

(5) As the brain was not examined, it was impossible to exclude a cerebro-vascular catastrophe.

(6) The experiments (although no doubt they impressed the jury) were not really scientific.

(7) Comparison of the post-mortem appearances seen in an animal shortly after death with those in a human body, dead for eleven days, is scarcely scientific.

(8) All the opinions were based on the evidence of Lady Boughton. These included the smell of the 'draught' and the victim's subsequent symptoms. These were not typical of prussic acid poisoning and it might be suggested that coronary artery disease could nowadays be added to the list of possible diseases.

The points made by John Hunter were quite simple :

(1) The post-mortem changes were those of putrefaction.

(2) The experiments were not only inadequate but showed lack of experience of experimental technique.

(3) Failure to examine the brain meant that a cerebro-vascular accident could not be excluded.

(4) Age and stature would not exclude it.

(5) Failure to examine the intestines showed fundamental lack of knowledge of the investigation of a case of poisoning.

Hunter alone was prepared to yield points in cross-examination and, above all, was prepared to admit that 'he did not know'. His deportment in the witness box could well be accepted as a model. It is of interest that Taylor comments on the following points :

(1) The practice of substituting poisonous mixtures for medical powders or draughts is not unusual but it might be supposed to indicate a degree of refinement and knowledge not commonly found amongst the lower class of criminals.

(2) In all cases it can never be presumed that the medicine taken is the cause of the symptoms unless we suppose it to be a poison.

(3) If there be the least doubt respecting the origin of the discolouration it would be unsafe to rely on it as evidence of poisoning.

(4) Danger of premature opinions—no opinion should be given until the whole of the analysis is complete.

It would seem that the following quotation from Paris and

Fonblanque (Vol 11, p401) is an appropriate postscript.

'Dr Price of Guildford having professed to have converted mercury into gold—put a period to his existence before the day appointed for his exhibition by a draught of laurel water. A mode of death no doubt suggested by the celebrated trial of Donellan the preceding year whose details it has been justly observed are not more important for the elucidation of the effects of poison, than for the strange display of professional testimony to which it gave origin.'

The research involved in the preparation of this paper has led me to believe that, from his teaching and precepts, John Hunter has offered a great contribution to Forensic Medicine. His own opinion of the Donellan case was:

'A poor devil was lately hanged upon no other testimony than that of physical men whose first experiments were made on this occasion.'

C

2 More about Jack the Ripper

THE STORY of the homicidal activities of Jack the Ripper during the autumn of 1888 is a perennial subject for books, articles and even films. His victims are far outnumbered by theories as to his identity (one goes so far as to question his sex, suggesting that 'Jack' should be supplanted by 'Jill'). Few of the theories hold water, however, and indeed in some instances the facts have been arbitrarily swept aside.

The following article was the result of the discovery in the basement of the London Hospital of original documents which were produced at the Coroner's Inquest on Catherine Eddowes. The injuries are confirmed in detail by old photographs now in the City of London Police Museum.

Exactly how many murders were actually the work of Jack the Ripper will remain one of the many uncertainties which are so often associated with crimes which are the subject of much publicity and sensationalism. The truth will be hidden by too much imagination and too little objectivity, in the same way that the real facts about even modern cases are confused by rules and regulations which result in inaccurate statements. It is for this reason that whether Catherine Eddowes was the fourth or fifth victim is of little consequence compared with the true information which it has yielded on an objective basis.

However, a brief reference to certain features which were common to the deaths of Mary Anne Nichols, Annie Chapman, Elizabeth Stride and Mary Jane Kelly, as well as Catherine Eddowes, are clearly of significance. All the women were prostitutes and alcoholics, and lived a precarious existence. They also shared in common wounds which had been inflicted with a sharp knife and yet were associated with far less spillage of blood than might have been expected. This is in direct contradiction with the fact that they were all stated to have died without crying out. The probable explanation may lie in a comment in a contemporary number of *The Lancet* that it was strange that their faces were congested under the circumstances, which suggests that the absence of a cry was due to strangulation being the real cause of death, a common practice of sexual murderers.

The other common feature was the close proximity of the scenes of the crime. To Eddowes, however, must go the distinction of being the only death which took place in the City of London. Perhaps less satisfactory from her point of view, she was the only victim whose life might have been saved. Her death also was the only occasion when a possible description of the assailant was available.

Catherine Eddowes, with her male associate Kelly, had followed a common practice in those days of going hop-picking in the country, but both had cut short this extra source of income to return to London on Thursday, 27 September 1888. It has been said that the reason for this was because they both anticipated obtaining the reward for identifying the 'Ripper'. In any event, by the time they had got back to London, they are said to have had just enough money to pay for a night's lodging together, whilst on the Friday night they lodged separately, he in a cheap doss-house and she in the casual ward in Mile End. On Saturday morning they were penniless and, after trying to get an odd job all the morning, they parted at 2 p.m. when Eddowes went off to Bermondsey to try and borrow money from her daughter, Annie. Nothing seems to be known of how she spent the next six hours, but at 8 p.m. she was arrested by two City policemen for being drunk and disorderly. In fact, she is said to have been standing in the middle of the road, imitating a fire engine, and was removed to Bishopsgate Police Station. There she remained until 12.30 a.m., singing to herself and asking to be released.

At about 1 a.m. her wish was complied with and she was shooed off into the night. When PC Watkins passed through the Square at 1.30 a.m. (see p113) he saw nothing unusual, but on his return about 15 minutes later he saw in the light of his lantern the body of a woman lying in the south-west corner (see p113). She was lying on her back, her left leg extended and her right leg bent at the knee. A description of the woman has appeared in many books but, thanks to the detective work of my assistant, Sam Hardy, who discovered, in the basement of The London Hospital, not only the plan (endorsed by the Coroner), but some pencil sketches made by the doctor at the scene (see p114), we have now an accurate record of the exact nature of the wounds and the position of the surrounding objects. Now one thing emerges from that night, if nothing else: the frustration of Major Smith, who was in a class above General Warren of the Metropolitan Police, at always being just behind the 'Ripper'. His route could be traced from Mitre Square across Houndsditch and Middlesex Street to Goulston Street, where, in a passage leading to a staircase of some flats, at 2.55 a.m., a PC Long of 'H' Division, Metropolitan Police, found a blood-stained rag which turned out to be a piece of Eddowes' apron, which had been cut off with a knife. Not only had it not been there at 2.20 a.m., but neither had a message, now found scrawled in chalk on a nearby doorway, saying: 'The Jewes are not the men to be blamed for nothing.'

As soon as Major Smith heard about this, he sent an Inspector with two detectives to photograph it—this General Warren not only refused to allow, *but he ordered the writing to be rubbed out at once.*

Meantime, whilst Dr F. G. Brown and Dr George Sequeira

were examining the body, the 'Ripper', having left Goulston Street, went north to Dorset Street, where he paused to wash blood off his hands at a public sink (this suggested he knew the neighbourhood as the sink was set back from the street).

Eddowes' body was removed to Golden Lane Mortuary where an inventory of her clothes, according to *The Times*, was as follows:

"She wore a black cloth jacket with imitation fur collar and three large metal buttons. Her dress is of dark green print, the pattern consisting of Michaelmas daisies and golden lilies. She also wore a thin white vest, a drab linsey skirt, and a very dark green alpaca petticoat, white chemise and brown ribbed stockings mended at the foot with white material. Her bonnet was black straw, trimmed with black beads and green and black velvet. She wore a pair of man's laced boots; and a piece of old white coarse apron and a piece of riband were tied loosely around the neck. There were also found upon her a piece of string, a common white handkerchief with a red border, a match-box with cotton in it, a white linen pocket containing a white bone handled table knife, very blunt (with no blood on it), two short clay pipes, a red cigarette case with white metal fittings ... a check pocket containing five pieces of soap, a small tin box containing tea and sugar, a portion of a pair of spectacles, a three-cornered check handkerchief, and a large white pocket containing a small comb, a red mitten and a ball of worsted."

Positive identification came from a small tin box which contained two pawnbrokers' tickets (for a man's flannel shirt and a pair of man's boots—pledged for 1s 6d each) in the names of Emily Burell and Anne Kelly. The body was stripped and an autopsy carried out but the body was not identified until Tuesday, 2 October, by John Kelly, who had been lulled into a false sense of security by the fact that one of his friends had seen Eddowes being taken to Bishopsgate Police Station. Her own (common law?) husband took two weeks to come forward, having changed his name to avoid being traced by her.

At the inquest, when it was stated by Lawende, a commercial traveller, that Eddowes had been seen talking to a man ten minutes before her death, the police requested that the description be witnessed. The description released was: 'Thirty years old, five feet nine inches in height, with a small fair moustache, dressed in something like navy serge and with a deerstalker's hat, peak fore and aft.' He also wore a red handkerchief.

Major Smith was conviced that it was an accurate description as it was bright moonlight at the time. When Dr Brown gave the results of his post-mortem examination, it was revealed for the first time that the left kidney was missing. On this fact, Dr Brown considered the assailant had anatomical skill, but this was disputed by Dr Sequera and Dr Saunders, who were right if the abdominal wound picture is correct (see p131).

Around the kidney is centred quite an extraordinary story, for Mr George Lusk, Chairman of the Whitechapel Vigilance Committee, received a parcel by post which was a cardboard box containing a portion of kidney with the following enclosure:

From hell

Mr. Lusk,
Sir,
    I send you half the kidne I took from one woman prasarved it for you, tother piece I fried and ate it was very nice. I may send you the bloody knif that took it out if you only wate a whil longer.

Signed
Catch me when you can, Mister Lusk.

Major Smith sent this to Dr Openshaw, Pathological Curator of The London Hospital Museum, for examination. He reported that it was a portion of human kidney, and that it had been placed in spirits within a few hours of its removal. It was a 'ginny kidney', ie, alcoholic, belonged to a woman of about 45, and had been removed within three weeks. Two inches of renal artery were in the body and one inch attached to the kidney. It is of interest that both the kidney left in the body and the 'postal' kidney showed severe Bright's disease.

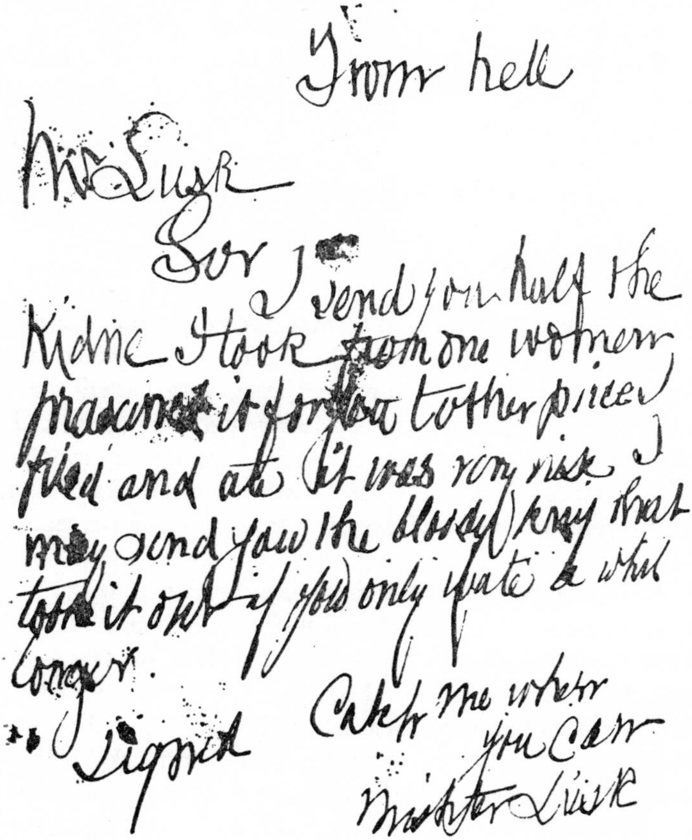

Fig 1
Facsimile of letter received with portion of kidney

3   Motives for Murder

THIS paper, which is adapted from a lecture given at the Galveston University Medical School, Texas, is dedicated to the memory of the late F. Tennyson Jesse, who culled the term 'murderee' in her brilliant book *Murder and Its Motives*. 'Fryn' Tennyson Jesse was one of England's greatest criminologists, and her introductions to several volumes in the series of *Notable British Trials* are masterpieces of observation and perception.

Miss F. Tennyson Jesse's name can be joined with those of Edmund Pearson and William Roughead as being the leading writers on criminology during the first half of this century. Tennyson Jesse, whom I first had the privilege to meet when she was preparing *Trials of Evans and Christie*[1] for the *Notable British Trials* series, was a writer with a remarkable skill in assessing the character of criminals, upon whose weaknesses she could, in most cases, unerringly put a finger. She had an encylopaedic knowledge of cases in the past and of weaknesses of the famous criminals. To this must be added an immense sense of humour, which she shared with Edmund Pearson of whom she was a great admirer. Two of the details associated with the Borden case[2] that were a constant amusement to her were the mutton soup for breakfast on the fatal day and the following doggerel:

> Lizzie Borden took an axe
> And gave her Mother forty whacks.
> When she saw what she had done
> She gave her Father forty-one.

Her liking for this she shared, it is alleged, with President Theodore Roosevelt.

Tennyson Jesse considered that there were six primary motives for murder:[3]

for Gain	for Jealousy
for Revenge	for Lust of Killing
for Elimination	for Conviction

These could possibly be compressed to:

for greed, jealousy, fear and hate,

although sometimes there may be a mixture, as is seen in the case of R. V. Attard[4] (noted later), a revenge killing which was a sequel to the murder of Big Audrey by Gopolan for jealousy.

In connection with murderers, Tennyson Jesse discussed what she calls the 'moral imbecile', which she is careful to point out is not necessarily synonymous with the 'moral defective'. She quotes Tredgold[5] as writing a new definition and says that the 'mental *defect*' of the definition was intended to denote, and does denote, a defect 'entirely different from the ordinary unintelligence of the feeble-minded or imbecile', for the moral imbecile is by no means unintelligent in the ordinary sense: he has wisdom which is combined in some cases with abnormal instincts and this is an essential characteristic of the class.

She quotes Mercier[6] as saying in this connection, 'however astute, clever, dextrous, intelligent, his shifts and dodges and stratagems and tricks may be, he is always a failure in the long run. He may succeed in his immediate object but his devious path soon leads him round into disaster. Usually the diameter lies so plainly before him that we wonder how a man so superficially clever should be beneath the surface such a fool. He takes the most careful measures against detection by one method and lays himself open to certain and speedy detection by another. He

has plenty of intelligence but little wisdom; he is a clever fool.'
Such modern characters as Haigh, Christie and Hume certainly
show this. Haigh, having brilliantly succeeded in liquidating
(literally) two complete families without its being even noticed,
for they had no proper roots, then selected, of all persons, a rich
elderly woman who was the regular member of a bridge four in
a Kensington hotel, whose absence was bound to be commented
upon. As though this were not enough, after dissolving her body
in acid he went no further than an adjoining town to dispose of
her property.[7] Christie's activities, though apparently for a different kind of gain, also involved the murder of girls who were not
likely to be missed or who, if their absence was reported to the
police, would be considered to have adequate reasons of their
own for disappearance. In his case, his surrender of the lease of
his rooms led to the discovery of the bodies, although it may be
said that he had good reason for leaving the house.[8] Hume, on
the other hand, appears to have been incapable of learning from
experience, or for that matter, appreciating his good fortune in
the Setty case.[9] He too appears to have repeated his method,
although on two former occasions it nearly led to his undoing
without much concrete gain.

Tennyson Jesse quotes as her own examples William Palmer[10]
and Neil Cream[11] (poisoners) and George Joseph Smith (the
brides in the bath).[12]

Before citing cases to illustrate the various motives which have
occurred in practice, there is one other observation for which
Miss Jesse must be given full credit. She suggests that, just as
certain people seem to be predestined to become murderers
under certain circumstances, others—it may be said because of
their stupidity in not appreciating what is going on—are destined
to be murdered: these she describes as born *murderees*. There
is considerable support for this theory; for example, in the case
of R. v Whybrow[13, 14] in which the man's wife, having forgiven
him once for bigamy, then finds evidence of yet another liaison;
with this she interferes, and yet when she receives an electric

shock under such unusual circumstances as being seated on the lavatory, she suspects nothing until she is lucky enough to survive a further shock from touching the soap dish which her husband has deliberately and ingeniously wired up to an electric power plug.

Of all the motives for murder, *gain* is the most common. Gain, however, is not limited to robbery for it may also include gain from inheritance (although this might be called elimination), to prevent loss of inheritance, or for sexual enjoyment of an unwilling party. For gain by robbery, a case of some interest was that of the boy Hyams[15] who murdered an old lady to obtain a few pounds in order to repay money given him by his schoolmates for fountain pens. This he had diverted from its proper use to purchase a 'make it yourself' model aeroplane kit. On his own admission, when pressed for the pens or the return of the money, he decided to go out and rob someone. This he did, striking down the first suitable victim and causing her death.

A further example of murder for gain occurred in 1959 (R. v Boswork and Jacobs).[16] This case, as in all the others, has an unusual aspect. A man named Folkard who was a night watchman at a printing works lived upon the premises. He had lost one eye and made a practice of going around the premises in the dark. One evening he joined his wife in bed rather later than usual and on turning on the light she found the front of his shirt to be smothered in blood from wounds on his scalp. He was unable to give any explanation for the injuries. The next morning he was in coma and was removed to a hospital for surgical treatment, which was unsuccessful. At autopsy he was found to have vertical lacerations on the scalp which at first sight seemed consistent with colliding with the edges of various racks. One wound on the side had been excised at operation and a fractured skull was revealed beneath it.

Examination of the works showed evidence of entry by a window. This was indicated by a palm print on a leather cushion, a thumb print on the window, and a foot print on the roof outside. Subsequently, routine examination of the palm prints of suspects detained by the police identified the owner, who admitted that he had been on the premises with another man who he alleged hit the watchman on the head with a printer's hammer. The second suspect proved to be in prison and had confided in his fellow residents that he had attacked Folkard. He was tried and convicted of capital murder but reprieved. The case is of interest as showing how easily injuries due to violence can be mistaken for accident.

Murder for revenge is represented in this collection of cases by one of more than ordinary interest. A professional tramp and scavenger called Adams, who had long white hair and a beard, lived in a room which he rented; he was most punctual in payment of his rent. In the autumn of 1957, as he was in arrears with his payments, entry was forced into his room and his body was found lying on the floor, somewhat decomposed and infected with larvae, with his head crushed and lying in a pool of blood. Examination of the front door downstairs showed splashes on the door and on each side. There was also blood smearing of the wall of the staircase. Examination of the skull of Adams showed obvious tangential cuts such as would be caused by a chopper. Later a man named Collier, living in the next room, was arrested and charged with murder. He admitted having seen Adams dead in his room on the day after he was missing. He gave, as explanation as to why he had told no one, that he had a criminal record and was frightened. The case was moreover complicated by the fact that several people came forward to say that they had seen Adams alive two weeks after he was supposed to be dead. It was, however, possible to establish an approximate time at which death had taken place from identification of the larvae and the stages of their development. Collier was convicted of capital murder (he was alleged to have taken some of Adams' money) but was reprieved after a petition which contained a full confession including the information that Adams had *walked* upstairs after being attacked with the chopper.[17] The reason for this murder was a desire for revenge by Collier because Adams had kicked his cat.

The second example of murder for revenge is 'the case of Big Audrey'. This lady practised the oldest profession in Poplar, in the East End of London. A man named Gopolan became enamoured with her and she visited him every Friday. He was disillusioned one day to find that he was not the only one upon whom she bestowed her favours. He accordingly set out armed with a knife, located her in a cafe sitting with her 'fiancée'— a Maltese gentleman called Attard—slipped inside, pushed her head forwards with one hand and neatly stabbed her in the back with the other, puncturing her aorta. He then disappeared down the road, hotly pursued by her friends who eventually caught him on a bombed side and felled him to the ground. One, somewhat over-enthusiastically, took the opportunity to hit his head with a piece of concrete lying near by. He was taken to The London Hospital where a craniotomy was performed, but in spite of this he died of a secondary pontine haemorrhage. At the subsequent trial[18] Big Audrey's friends were acquitted of all charges.

Murder for elimination is represented in this series by two cases of different character. 'The case of the happy sergeant' occurred in Duisburg, Germany, and involved the exhumation of a dead man upon whom a court of enquiry had returned a decision of *suicide*. When, however, eight months later Emmett Dunne married the widow, the case was reopened and from the appearances of photographs taken the day after the death, it appeared that the hanging had been faked as there was congestion both above and below the mark of suspension. Also a most unusual injury was a fracture of the thyroid cartilage in the mid line. Experiments showed that this could be due to an unarmed combat blow on the neck. Later Emmett, a stepbrother of Emmett Dunne, made a statement to the effect that he had helped his stepbrother to hang up Watters *after* death. The trial by General Court Martial took place in Dusseldorf and resulted in conviction of Emmett Dunne.[19]

The second case was that of the killing by Mrs Christophi of her daughter-in-law in order that she should remain in England. The background of the case is important. Mrs Christophi was a Cypriot whose son, a very successful waiter in England, had married a German refugee. The mother, who was almost a classical picture of the matriarch, came to England on the guarantee of her son. It was not very long before she tried to rule the house, a manoeuvre which was naturally resented by the daughter-in-law. As it appeared quite an insoluble problem, the son told his mother to return to Cyprus, saying that he would withdraw his guarantee for her residence in England. Shortly after this Mrs Christophi hailed a passing car outside her front door one night and told the driver that her daughter-in-law had come to harm from fire. It required no more than a cursory examination of the body, which was lying in the back yard behind the house, to decide she was dead and that she had not burnt herself. The body, which appeared to have been soaked in paraffin, was severely charred, and examination of the neck showed the mark of a scarf which had been present during the fire and removed afterwards, cutting the skin. At autopsy, an extensive fracture of the skull was seen, involving the occipital bone and the base. Reconstruction showed that apparently the lady had first been hit by a heavy weapon (probably the front of the grate). After this the scarf was applied tightly and the body ignited. The investigation of the case was assisted by a neighbour who had seen a fire and looked down into the yard to see Mrs Christophi stoking it. 'The case of the burning lady' ended in the conviction of Mrs Christophi at the Central Criminal Court[20] and her subsequent execution. Information was received that in the past, in Cyprus, she had been acquitted of a somewhat similar charge.

Of all motives, *jealousy* is probably the most intense, and although often misplanned has led to the most dramatic cases such as R. v Ley and Smith[21] when Ley, a London businessman who had once been prominent in politics in his native Australia, was convicted of the murder of a barman called Mudie whom he believed to be seducing his mistress.

The first case of interest in my series is 'the case of the body in the boot' when Ozolins, a Pole, was convicted of murder of another Pole and of disposing of his body by dumping it by the roadside. The injuries were interesting, consisting of a severe crush injury of the skull and also of the chest, due, it was alleged by the prosecution, to deliberately running the man over with a car. The evidence of dumping was supplied by a completely dry mackintosh beneath the body, although since early evening it had been raining heavily. The exact place of the murder was never identified, but two important pieces of evidence undoubtedly helped to decide the case—firstly, an alibi of a visit to a public house which had clearly not taken place, and secondly, the chance that a doctor happened to be passing the spot where the body was dumped and recognised the car.[22]

The case of Hume, 'the flying smuggler', needs little recapitulation as it has been published and more recently revived by the exploits of the central figure in Switzerland, where he is now serving a life sentence for the murder of a Zurich taxi-driver. It was chiefly remarkable on acccount of the method of disposal of the body by cutting it up and throwing the pieces from an aeroplane. Hume finally pleaded guilty to a lesser charge after a retrial (the first trial was stopped because of the illness of the Judge) and disagreement of the jury.[9] On his release from prison, Hume wrote a confession of guilt for a newspaper.

Murders from *lust of killing* when the murderer is fully sane must be rare. John Reginald Christie appears to have pursued a most consistent path of premeditated murder in order to satisfy his sexual desire. Finally, he proved true to type by leaving his house where he alone could preserve his guilty secret. As was inevitable, another occupant of the house commenced to clean up the flat. On stripping the wall-paper he discovered a cupboard containing the bodies of three women. Later search revealed another body (Christie's wife) beneath the floor boards of the front room and two skeletons in the garden as evidence of his earlier frolics. The fact that a man called Evans was convicted and executed for the murder of his baby daughter in the same house between the first and second periods of Christie's activities, certainly caused more controversy than has been seen for a long time and undoubtedly aided the abolition of the death penalty.[1, 8]

Finally, there is the *murder from conviction*. Probably the best example of recent years in England was that for which Fantle was convicted.

The two cases in this series might be otherwise classified but can nevertheless be included in this category. In the first case a child who had been missing for 24 hours was found dead in a bomb-damaged house. The motive was really elimination, for the woman who killed the child is believed to have done so in order to have her husband executed. She got the child into the house and killed it with a hammer. In the process, whilst gripping the child, she inflicted grouped linear bruises and abrasions on the child's chest, which ultimately were her undoing for examination of her finger nails showed wool fibres similar to those of the child's jumper.[23]

The second example is a case of what has been aptly described as a typical 'kitchen sink' murder. A spinster who went to stay for a short time with her sister-in-law, Mrs Chubb, remained as a permanent lodger at a very low charge. In addition she imposed upon the unfortunate woman to such an extent that one morning Mrs Chubb, unable to bear it any more as she saw her 'arrogant sister-in-law' going towards the front door, seized her scarf from behind and pulled it tight around her neck. The untimely visit of the postman made death quite inevitable, for to stop any cry she placed her hand over the woman's face. This behaviour could well be the outcome of grievous provocation but the next manoeuvre showed considerable presence of mind, for she placed the body in an invalid chair, concealed it in a shed and in the early hours of the next morning dumped it by the roadside to look like a motor accident. Her success was frustrated by the presence on the wrong surface of the body of a linear mark of pressure whitening across the back of the leg.[24]

All these cases bear out the theories of Tennyson Jesse and in addition have at least one point of original interest to those whose profession it is to practise the detection of crime.

REFERENCES

1 Jesse, F. Tennyson (ed). Notable British Trials—Trials of Evans and Christie. Hodge, Edinburgh, 1957.
2 Pearson, Edmund Lester. Studies in Murder. Macmillan, New York, 1924.
3 Jesse, F. Tennyson. Murder and its Motives. Harrap, London, 1952.
4 R. v Attard. Central Criminal Court, 1958.
5 Tredgold, A. F. Mental Deficiency.
6 Mercier, C. Conduct and its Disorders; Crime and Criminals; Criminal Responsibility.
7 Dunboyne, Lord (ed). Notable British Trials—Trial of J. G. Haigh. Hodge, Edinburgh, 1953.
8 Camps, Francis E. Medical and Scientific Investigation in the Christie Case. Medical Publications Ltd, London, 1953.
9 R. v Hume. Central Criminal Court, 1949.
10 Watson, Eric R. (ed). Notable British Trials—Trial of William Palmer. Hodge, Edinburgh, 1952.
11 Shore, W. Teignmouth (ed). Notable British Trials—Trial of Neil Cream. Hodge, Edinburgh, 1923.
12 Watson, Eric R. (ed). Notable British Trials—Trial of George Joseph Smith, 1949.
13 R. v Whybrow. Essex Assizes, 1952.
14 Camps, F. E. and Purchase, W. P. B. Practical Forensic Medicine, Medical Publications Ltd, 1956.
15 R. v Hyams. Central Criminal Court, 1957.
16 R. v Bosworth and Jacobs. Central Criminal Court, 1959.
17 R. v Collier. Central Criminal Court, 1958.
18 R. v Attard. Central Criminal Court, 1958.
19 R. v Emmett Dunne. General Court Martial, Dusseldorf, 1955.
20 R. v Christophi. Central Criminal Court, 1954.
21 Roberts, C. E. Bechhoffer (ed). The Trial of Ley and Smith. Jarrolds, London, 1947.
22 R. v Ozolins. Central Criminal Court, 1957.
23 R. v Tierney. Central Criminal Court, 1948.
24 R. v Chubb. Central Criminal Court, 1958.

D

4   The Colchester Taxi Cab Murder

THIS case, which involved the murder of an English cab driver by US soldiers during World War II, is a tribute to the unflurried and painstaking methods of Detective Chief Superintendent George Totterdell, Head of the Essex County Constabulary Criminal Investigations Department, to whom I owe most of my basic initiation into the investigation of murder. The case provides a remarkable example of co-operation between the English police and the US Army CID.

In introducing this case it will be helpful if I give a short description of the district in which the murder took place. Colchester is a garrison town in Essex situated about 50 miles from London and about 20 miles from Chelmsford. Maldon is a small port and town situated about 17 miles south-east of Colchester. The main road from Colchester to Maldon passes through Tiptree, and just to the Colchester side is Birch, where a large aerodrome was being built at the time of this crime. The work was being done by about 5,000 coloured American troops stationed close to the site and it is between Birch and Colchester that the majority of the incidents to be described took place. During the period now under review, taxis were the only means of public transport at night between Colchester and Birch, although the military authorities ran lorries and cars, and there is reason to believe that taxi charges were based upon the well known law of supply and demand. Apart from the main Maldon-Colchester road which passes through Birch and Tiptree there is also a lower road to Maldon which goes through Tolleshunt D'Arcy. The whole of the district is subject to winter mists and fogs.

The case was investigated throughout by the Essex County Constabulary although the accused were handed over to the American authorities for trial. On 8 December 1943, a message was received at the headquarters of the Essex County Constabulary at Chelmsford reporting that a taxi cab with its side lights still on had been found at 11.30 a.m. in Haynes Green Lane, Layer Marney, near Birch Aerodrome, and that the driver, a man named Claude Hailstone, was missing. The inside of the car showed evidence of a struggle and in the back seat were a blood-stained mackintosh and a blue jacket with its sleeve inside out; these were identified later by Mrs Pearse, his landlady, as being the property of Hailstone.

Enquiries about the car and Hailstone's movements on the previous day showed that at 10 p.m. he called at his garage, saw the proprietor and collected a spare wheel; he then had two white American soldiers sitting in the back seat, and left saying 'I must rush off as I have an order for Stanway.' At 10.10 p.m. he called at the Woodside Club, Great Horkesley, picked up two officers and drove them to the Public Library, Colchester, getting there about 10.30 p.m. The last time he called at his lodgings (127 Maldon Road, Colchester) was at 11-11.10 p.m. to tell his landlady that he had no time to stop for supper as he had a 'job' for Birch. He said that he had as passengers a black officer and a private and that he would be back in half an hour. The car was then heard to start up and go in the direction of Birch. Hailstone himself was not seen again but at 11.30 p.m. a coloured officer, Lieutenant Bowman, saw a taxi cab stationary on the offside of the road at Haynes Green Lane, Layer Marney, and at midnight another coloured soldier, Private John Carr, whilst walking from Feering to Messing passed a telephone box outside the 'Crown

Inn' and saw a man inside talking on the telephone. He went on towards Birch Camp and about ¼ mile from the kiosk came upon an unattended taxi cab CPU 620 on the nearside of the road facing towards Birch. Inside on the rear seat he noticed a blood-stained raincoat and a jacket with one sleeve turned inside out. Hearing footsteps approaching he went to his hut some 100 yards away and heard a car engine start up and go in the direction of Birch Camp.

In the course of the enquiry another significant report was received from Charles Barbrook who, whilst cycling to work at 6.15 a.m., had seen a bloodstained mackintosh lying in the near-side gutter 40 yards on the Tollesbury side of Tolleshunt D'Arcy and had left it there and reported his discovery to the police. When, however, a police officer went to the spot three-quarters of an hour later it had disappeared. The next day (9 December 1943) a man named Lawrence was stopped and he handed over a mackintosh which he admitted having picked up near Tolleshunt D'Arcy the previous morning. It was found to be heavily blood-stained in front. The stains were examined by Dr Davidson at the Police Laboratory, Hendon, and proved to be Group AB; these stains were on the front (left), right sleeve, right shoulder. The garment itself was of the type issued to Canadian officers, and was marked on the inside 'J. J. Weber'.

At daybreak on 9 December a search was organised with the assistance of the military authorities of the whole area in the neighbourhood of Birch Camp, and at 12.55 p.m. PC Snowling discovered the body of Hailstone lying amongst the brambles on the far side of a 4ft bank in the grounds of Birch Rectory on the main Colchester-Birch road. It had been pushed under the strands of a barbed wire fence which showed some drops of blood, and could not be seen from the road. The body was photographed in its original position and I saw it later. It was fully clothed with the exception of a jacket, the head was pointing towards Maldon and the left side of the face showed bruising with much blood soiling. A provisional opinion of manual strangulation was based upon typical finger nail impressions and scratches on the neck with haemorrhages into the whites of the eyes. The position of the body and rivulets of blood were in keeping with the body having rolled down the slope after death, which had occurred at least 24 hours previously.

After my examination the body was moved to Colchester Public Mortuary where a post-mortem examination was performed. The clothing yielded the sum of £2 18s 6d in silver and two £1 notes were found in the waistcoat pockets. It was believed that Hailstone kept his money there because he had claw hands and this had caused the money to be overlooked. The findings may be summarised as follows:

(1) The man was healthy and of good physique (height 5ft 7in), but had a deformity of both hands (claw hands) which would make him less able to defend himself. There was no evidence on the body that he had offered any resistance.

(2) The left eye was bruised and also the left side of the nose, mouth and chin, indicating at least three heavy blows with some object such as a fist.

(3) There were abrasions on both sides of the neck in front, these being more marked upon the right side but with underlying bruising more marked on the left side. There was a fracture of the left upper cornu of the thyroid cartilage.

The marks on the neck were characteristically those of a gripping hand, the fingers being on the right side with duplication due to slipping and reapplication of pressure. The direction indicated the tips of the fingers to the back. The semicircular marks on the left side of the neck could be fairly accurately measured and were about 7/10in long; they also indicated reapplication.

(4) Superficial abrasions with bruising on the front of the right knee, right shin and left shin; abrasions of this kind usually result from contact with the dashboard of a motor car when the body is projected backwards.

(5) Bruising of the left shoulder with abrasions and a bruise on the top of the scalp in keeping with the head and shoulder having been struck by or come in contact with a blunt object.

(6) Scratch marks which had taken place after death and which could well have been caused by contact with brambles or thorns.

From this examination it was possible to say that Hailstone had been strangled from behind with a left hand and also struck upon the face. The grazing of the front of the shins suggested that he was pushed backwards whilst sitting in the front seat of the car.

Blood taken from the body was grouped by Dr Davidson at the Metropolitan Police Laboratory and proved to be Group AB. Scrapings taken from all the nails of both hands were reported as follows:

> "The scrapings from the nails of the third and fifth fingers of the right hand showed the presence of blue fibres. Scrapings from the nails of the first and second fingers of the left hand showed the presence of blue and pink fibres."

Blood scraped from the palm of Hailstone's right hand belonged to Group AB and the blood stains on Hailstone's coat found in the taxi were also Group AB. As I have already said, the mackintosh found on the roadside with the name 'J. J. Weber' inside it, was heavily bloodstained with Group AB blood.

Enquiries were made of the Canadian Army as to the identity of 'Weber' and at first no record could be traced but later it was found to be the property of Captain J. J. Weber of 18th Canadian General Hospital, Colchester. This officer was traced to Uckfield in Sussex. He was interviewed and made the following statement:

> "At about 2.30 p.m. on Sunday, December 5, 1943, I was on the platform at Liverpool Street Station waiting to catch the 4 o'clock train to Colchester when I started talking to a partly coloured American soldier who was standing there. He was alone and had sergeant's stripes on his overcoat. I am certain he was wearing a topcoat with stripes on the sleeves and was wearing a peaked cap. He was carrying a service respirator. He told me he was waiting for a train for Colchester. We went into the Buffet

and had two or three beers each and spoke about things generally, chiefly about Canada.

"We continued talking together and travelled down together on the 4 o'clock train to Colchester. On arrival there I hired a taxi and invited him to come along with me to Cherry Tree Camp, Colchester, where the 18th Canadian General Hospital is, to have a drink. I paid the driver and we went into Major Savage's room. Major Savage was away and this room is the only one that has a stove and bed made up in it. It would be then about 6 p.m. and the American soldier had told the taxi driver to come back for him in about an hour's time.

"I then got a full bottle of whiskey, a round shaped bottle, lock neck, believed 'Dewars Scotch Whiskey', imperial pint size but which we call a quart, from the officers' mess, and we had some drinks out of it. In the meantime I had taken off my raincoat and laid it on the bed. After about half an hour I went to the bathroom leaving the American in the room. By this time I was beginning to feel happy, but was not drunk. I was away about ten minutes and when I came back to the room the sergeant had gone. I don't know how much whiskey was drunk or what was left in the bottle when the American sergeant took it away, but we only consumed two or three drinks each. The man had left his respirator behind. I did not pay any attention to this as I knew he had ordered the taxi and this may have arrived while I was away. He had previously told me he was stationed near Colchester. I did not notice anything missing then and I sat down in a chair and dozed off to sleep. About 10 p.m. the same night I woke up and went to get my coat and could not find it and also the bottle of whiskey had gone. I then went across to the officers' mess in Cherry Tree Camp and later went to bed. The next morning I reported to the officers' mess sergeant and later the same morning I went to Fleet, Hampshire.

"In the pockets of the raincoat I had the following property: gent's Rolex victory wristwatch, white metal, about the size of a halfpenny, 24 hours with a sweep second hand. Back unscrews with a special type of spanner, on a worn brown leather strap. Pair of gent's brown leather gloves, ordinary kid, old condition, press stud fastener on wrist, size 7½. Ordinary khaki handkerchief bearing my name 'J. J. Weber' in black ink. Five one pound notes, new condition, loose in my pocket, which I put there when I got the bottle of whiskey from the officers' mess. Return half railway ticket to Hayward's Heath from Colchester.

"I certainly did *not* give my coat or any money to this American soldier and he did not ask me for any either. I had never seen him before that day or since. I did not ask him his name and he did not tell me. He said he came from the Southern part of the States. I would describe this American soldier as aged about 30 years, height 5ft 10in, weight about 160lbs. Average build, dark hair and eyes, dark complexion as of part Negro, slight thin strip moustache, straight nose, good teeth. I could identify this man again.

"The American soldier asked the taxi driver to come back and pick him up or send another one. I did not ask him to stay. The raincoat was the only top coat I had with me at the time and I certainly would not have given him that. I may have had some drink but I knew what I was doing. If the man says I gave him the coat and some money he is telling lies."

He was later (14 December 1943) shown a pencil torch which was found outside the cells in Colchester Police Station and identified it as his property which had been in his coat at Cherry Tree Camp. He also said:

"The raincoat now shown to me marked 'J. J. Weber' is my property and the one I missed from Major Savage's room at the Cherry Tree Camp, Colchester. I have been shown the watch produced and it is my property and the one which was in my raincoat pocket when it was stolen. I value the whole property at £18 15s 0d."

The respirator which was left behind by the coloured soldier in Captain Weber's room was identified by Private Hall of RCAMC who noticed it in his hand on his arrival and was later handed the respirator by Captain Weber. He in his turn had handed it to Superintendent Totterdell on 12 December 1943. This gas mask had inside it the name 'Hill' and was identified as belonging to a Private Soloman Hill (a coloured engineer) who, when interviewed, admitted that it was his property and said that he had lent it to another coloured man, Private George Fowler. Fowler denied all knowledge of the murder but on searching his belongings a sergeant's tunic was found hanging over his bed showing blood stains and in his kitbag was found an envelope containing several papers amongst which were a pawn ticket for a Rolex Victory watch pawned upon 6 December 1943 for £3 at W. J. Hyde, Pawnbrokers, of 117 Catton Street, London, E.1, and papers relating to a loan of 10s from American Red Cross on 7 December 1943.

Fowler then made a statement to the effect that on 1 December he went on pass to London with some other men. He had on an OD hat and a private's blouse which he had borrowed. He was carrying a gas mask which belonged to Private A. O. Hill. He was not wearing an overcoat. On reaching London he went to the Liberty Club, Euston Street, where he booked a room and left his gas mask. He spent the nights of 1 and 2 December at the Liberty Club, and he gave a detailed description of his movements, most of which were in the West End and said that he slept the night of 3 December with a girl in Chepstow Street. He also *thought* he spent the night of 4 December there and the night of 5 December he was positive he spent in London although he could not say where. On 6 December he picked up a girl at 5 p.m. and went home with her for the night, but could not say where she lived and gave only a vague description of her. On the morning of 7 December, he said he continued his round of pubs and clubs, ending up at the Florida Club where he picked up a girl with whom he stayed the night; in this case he could only give a vague description of the place but gave a very detailed description of the girl who was called Helen, was about 22 years, 5ft 4in in height and weighed 122lbs. He said that he did not remember leaving Helen's house or having any breakfast on the morning of 8 December, and gave as his reason that he was drunk the night before or might even have been doped. In fact the next he knew was being in camp at Birch at 9.45 a.m. on his own bed, but he did remember some American soldiers bringing him home and that when he woke up he had on a shirt with three stripes.

When asked to account for the gas mask he said he had not returned it but intended to do so and that it was under the bed in his billet; he also said he had seen Hill and had promised to return it and that he had last seen it under his bed that morning. He denied having been in the company of a Canadian officer whilst on leave. He said that he should have returned on 3 December and did not get back until 8 December and had been punished for that. He then said he wanted to alter his story about the gas mask and that he had checked it at the Liberty Club on 1 December and received a ticket and that he now found the gas mask was not there and had told Hill that he had lost it and would get him another. He stated that he had never pawned a watch in his life and had not got a watch nor had he had any dealings with anybody over a watch. He had not seen a pawn ticket since he was in this country.

On being shown an envelope (which bore the name of Huntley) by Detective Superintendent Totterdell he said he had found it on the floor of the West Indies Club. It was sealed up when found. He had opened it and seen a card inside but he had not taken the card out. He recognised two 'guest of Liberty Club' cards bearing his name, a Red Cross acknowledgement form bearing his signature, a guest receipt No AGO 4470 and a piece of paper with 'Provost Marshal, 96 Piccadilly' written on it. These he had put in the envelope on either 3 or 4 December, on one of which days he picked it up. The guest ticket was given to him at the Liberty Club and authorised him to occupy Room 144, Bed No 36, on 7 December 1943. After the ticket was made out he told the lady he would be coming back on 8 December and she wrote 7 and 8 December on the back and amended it on the front to read 7/8/12/43 but he did not stay there on those nights.

The piece of paper bearing 'Provost Marshal, 96 Piccadilly' and 'ARC Field Office, 13 Grosvenor Square (Basement) Mr Beackman' he said he had written. The words Provost Marshal on this were for an American who had asked him for the address. The lady at the Liberty Club had written the bottom part. He then went on to say, 'The reason I did not give the American soldier the piece of paper after I had written the Provost Marshal's address down was that he asked me to write it down as he could not understand me.' He was then asked to write down the 'Provost Marshal' note but was unable even to spell the words. Another obvious discrepancy was the fact that he said he found the pawn ticket on 3 or 4 December whilst the watch was not pawned until the 6th. The man was quite obviously lying and he was interrogated for some time but adhered to his story.

In view of the fact that his description tallied with that given by Captain Weber of the man who had taken his coat and also the fact he was wearing sergeant's stripes he was detained on suspicion. Meanwhile a statement was taken from another coloured soldier named Huntley (whose name was on the envelope) and he admitted being in London on 6 December where he met a coloured soldier named Leatherberry who gave him a watch at the West Indian Club and asked him whether he knew a place to pawn it. He stated that he himself had taken the watch to a pawnbroker, W. J. Hyde, and obtained £3 on it which he later gave to 'George'. He had received the pawn ticket in a sealed envelope and gave it to 'George' at the same time as the money. On 13 December Fowler was again questioned and made a voluntary statement under caution:

Statement of George E. Fowler, dated 13 December 1943.
"On December 1, 1943, I left Camp with three other soldiers and went to London on pass. I had a 48-hour pass and I was supposed to be back in Camp at 12.00 hrs, December 3, 1943. I did not return to Camp until December 8, 1943. For being A.W.O.L. I was tried in a Summary Court and fined $25 and given two weeks confinement to Camp on December 8, 1943. I stayed in London from December 1, 1943, until December 5, 1943. I went to Liverpool Street Station, London, to catch the train which left for Colchester at 14.15 hrs. While waiting in the Liverpool Street Station I met a British Captain (Army) and we had a few drinks together in the Station pub. We took the 14.15 hrs train to Colchester together and when we arrived at Colchester he asked me to come to his Camp which was the Cherry Tree Camp for a few drinks. The Captain paid the taxi fare to Cherry Tree Camp from Colchester. I went to a room in the Captain's hut with him and he only left the room once while I was there and this time he went to get some liquor which he brought back with him. I stayed with the Captain in his hut for about an hour. At some time during this hour the Captain gave me his raincoat and a short while after he gave me this he passed out as he had had too much to drink. I carried the raincoat out of the hut with me. Before I left the hut the Captain had passed

out and someone came into the room and asked me to sober him up and get him to go to his room. I could not sober him up and left while the Captain was still 'out'. When I left the hut I left my gas mask which I borrowed from Private Hill, who is in the hut I sleep in, in the Captain's hut. I borrowed this gas mask from Private Hill on December 1, 1943, and I intended to return it to him when I got back to Camp. I did not mean to leave it in Captain Weber's hut. This gas mask had Private Hill's name on it. I have been shown, and have identified, this gas mask since I left it in the hut.

"I took the bus from Cherry Tree Camp to the Colchester bus terminal and while waiting there for a bus to Messing I put on the coat which the Captain gave me. When I put the coat on I felt something in the pockets but did not pay attention to what it was. I took a bus from Colchester back toward Camp and got off at the White Horse Pub, near Birch, with some other soldiers. I went into this pub and drank some liquor from a bottle which I bought from a man in the Colchester Bus Station while waiting for the bus. I drank with a fellow who said he was in Co A of 356th Engineer Regiment, who asked me to go back to London with him.

"I reached the White Horse Pub at about 19.00 hrs, 5/12/43, and left there with the soldier at about 20.30 hrs and headed for London. We caught a jeep going to Colchester and from there took a train to London where we arrived about 23.00 hrs. We spent the night together in a rooming house in the East End of London. I wore the coat given to me by the British Captain in London.

"On December 5, 1943, before I got on the train going back to London, I put hands in the pocket of the raincoat and found in there a wrist watch and a pencil flashlight. This is all I found in the pockets. I knew that the Captain did not intend to give these to me.

"On December 6, 1943, I met Private Huntley, who is from the same Camp I am from, and I asked him to pawn the wrist watch which I found in the Captain's raincoat for me. He did this and gave me the pawn ticket and two of the three pounds he received as a result of pawning the watch. He kept the other pound himself. Private Huntley did not know where I got the watch as I did not tell him. I did not intend to return the watch or the flashlight which I identified on December 17, 1943, as being the flashlight I took from the Captain's raincoat pocket, back to the Captain. I pawned the watch because I needed some money.

"On December 7, 1943, I met the soldier at about 18.00 hrs

and told him that I was going back to Camp. He said that he
would go back with me. We took the 20.45 hrs train from Liverpool Street Station to Colchester and arrived at Colchester at
about 22.20 hrs. On the way up on the train from London to
Colchester, Leatherberry continually told me that he needed
some money, he said that he was broke and going to get it any
way he could get it. When we got off the train at Colchester he
said that he was cold so I gave him the Captain's raincoat to
wear. We then hired a taxi. When we were on the train from
London, Leatherberry said that we could rob a taxi driver in the
taxi which we were going to take from the Colchester Railroad
Station back to Camp.

"After we took the taxi from the Station it stopped somewhere
in Colchester and the taxi driver went into a house and told us to
wait outside and he would be right out. When the driver was
inside this house he said that he was going to have him stop by
the side of the road and he was going to rob him. When the taxi
driver went into the house, Leatherberry thought that he was
going in for a gun. The taxi driver came out of the house in a few
minutes and drove on toward Birch. When we were about four
miles from Colchester, going toward Birch, the taxi driver stopped
the cab as he stopped him when he told the driver he wanted to
take a leak. The driver stopped the cab on the left-hand side of
the road as we came from Colchester. As I was sitting in the
left-hand rear seat I got out of the left-hand rear door to have a
leak. He stayed in the taxi. While I was outside having a leak I
heard a struggle and he called to me and asked me if I was going
to help him and I did not answer.

"After I finished taking the leak I came back into the rear of
the cab and he had the cab driver by the throat with his hands
and was pounding him with the other hand. When I got completely into the cab the driver was limp. The upper part of the
driver's body was over the front seat and the lower part of his
body was in the front seat. He asked me to help him get the body
out of the taxi and we had to get away from there. He was going
through the taxi driver's pockets when he asked me to help him
get the body out of the taxi. He told me that I was in this just
as much as he was. He had on the Captain's raincoat at this time
and he had some papers, a bill fold, and a lighter in his hands.
He took hold of the driver's shoulders and pulled him out of the
rear right door, and I took hold of the driver's feet and we carried
him across the street, and pushed him under a wire fence. I
think that he put the papers, bill fold and lighter in his pocket.
I did not see him throw anything away.

"We crossed the street from the place where we left the body and I got behind the driver's wheel and he sat beside me in the front seat. I drove about a tenth of a mile toward Camp and he said that he wanted to drive to Maldon. I got out of the driver's seat and let him drive. He drove to Maldon and I was with him. He stopped the cab in Maldon and we got out and walked up the street. He stopped a Policeman with a Bobbie's helmet on and asked him what time the train left Maldon for London. He was told that there were not any trains for London that night. After we left the Bobbie I told him that I was going back to Camp and he said that I was doing wrong. I went to the cab and he came with me and I drove back toward Camp. On the way back to Camp he told me to park the cab along the road some place. I attempted to pull off the road and as I started down a road someone spotted a flashlight on the taxi and I pulled out. I don't know who had the flashlight. I then drove the cab down the road a little farther and parked it on the road to Company 'C'. I turned the headlights off and might have left the parking lights on.

"We got out of the taxi and went to my hut in Company 'E' where the boys were shooting craps. He said that this was no place for us to be so we left about five minutes later and we went to the guard tent in Company 'B'. It was his suggestion. I slept that night in a lower bunk on the left-hand side of the tent and he slept on the right-hand side in an upper bunk. I went to sleep and the next morning I left the guard tent at about 08.00 hrs. I don't know when he left the tent. I don't know whether or not he was there when I left. I went to my Company and laid down on my own bed and went to sleep. The Charge of Quarters woke me and told me that the Company Commander wanted me. I went to the Company Commander after the Charge of Quarters came and got me the second time. I do not know what happened to the raincoat the Captain gave me as I do not remember seeing it after we left the body. The cigarette lighter which he took from the driver's body I saw in his possession the night of 9/12/43 when he came to my hut and told me that he had heard that the taxi driver was dead.

"We did not know whether or not the taxi driver was dead when we left him. He was unconscious. I have read my statement of 11¼ pages and it is true."

Enquiries had already been made at Colchester Station and were repeated but nobody could remember seeing either man on the train leaving Liverpool Street at 8.45 p.m. (Colchester 10.26). This was not surprising as there were about 5,000 coloured troops in the area and to strangers they all look more or less alike.

On 13 December, Leatherberry was interviewed and made the following statement:

Statement of J. C. Leatherberry dated 13 December 1943.
"I left Camp on 5/12/43 at about 16.00 hrs. I had a pass which lasted from the time I left Camp until 23.00 hrs 5/12/43. I walked up to the White Horse Pub alone and when I was there I met a fellow named Funlely who was from 'E' Co of the 356th Engineer Regt. Funlely had a quart of scotch with him and some of it had been drunk. There was about half the bottle gone when he showed it to me. Inside the pub he and I had some drinks out of the bottle and we drank all the liquor in the bottle with the exception of some of it which a friend of Funlely's drank. After we finished the liquor we left the bottle on the table. The bottle was a bottle with six or eight corners on it. I do not remember what kind of liquor it was but I know it was whiskey. I left the White Horse Pub with Funlely and went to London with him. He told me that he had been on pass but his pass was up and he and I kidded each other saying that the other would not go back to London. Finally we caught a ride in a jeep to Colchester and from there we got a train to London.

"I was drunk and I arrived in London about 22.00 hours and I do not remember what happened that night but the next morning, 6/12/43, I woke up in the Rowton House, Christian Street, East London. Funlely was in the same house with me when I woke up the next morning. When I met Funlely the next morning, 6/12/43, he told me that I had heaved on his blouse and he had to bring it to the Red Cross in the West side. He did not have a blouse on on Monday morning and when he left me at 10.30 hrs he said that he was going to get it. I am not sure that he had on a G.I. overcoat but I think he did. I did not see Funlely again until about 19.00 hrs or 20.00 hrs that night. He left me that night to stay with a girl and I did not see him again until 7/12/43 at about 17.00 hrs. I met him at Sam's Bar on Cable Street in the East End. He was with a girl and I was with a girl named Eva, who I met at Sam's Bar. After the movies I left Eva and went to Freddie's house on Bigland Street where I spent the night with some soldiers. Some of the soldiers I stayed with that night were Huntley from 'F' Company, Edward Harris from 'F' Company, and another soldier whose name I do not know. There were some other soldiers there but I don't know their names. Funlely spent the night with some girl on the West side of London. I met Funlely, 8/12/43, at Morri's Cafe on Cable Street, at about 09.00 hrs. He was then wearing the same blouse he had on when he left Camp. He did not have any kind of a coat with him then.

At about 10.25 he and I and four other fellows took a train from Liverpool Street Station back to Colchester. We caught a bus from Colchester to Camp. I arrived at Camp at about 13.00 hrs and went right to my Company. Funlely and some other fellows who were on the bus with me left me at a fork in the road near the 816 Engineer Co, at Camp. I was dressed in a class 'A' uniform when I left Camp and I had the same uniform on when I came back to Camp. I have read my statement of 3¾ pages and it is true."

It will be noticed that he refers to Fowler as 'Funlely' and confirms their meeting on 5 December; denies being with him on 7 December but says that he spent the night at 'Freddie's house'.

He was detained and his kit was searched, and in his bag was found:

(1)   A shirt with blood stains inside the cuffs.

(2)   Uniform trousers showing faint blood stains on the inner surface of the right fly opening, and mud-staining down the front and sides of both legs.

(3)   A pair of pants with blood-staining on the inner and outer surfaces of both sides of the fly opening and at the top of the waist band.

(4)   A vest showing blood stains in the midline of the front near the lower hem.

Examination of the blood stains at the Police Laboratory showed the blood stains on the shirt and trousers to be human blood but insufficient for grouping, but the stains on the pants were Group AB. On 14 December Leatherberry was again questioned and his finger prints were taken. He maintained his original story and declined to make any further statement. During the day Captain Weber identified the watch which had been pawned as his property and also the torch which had been found outside Fowler's cell at Colchester police station.

On the following day an identification parade was held and Leatherberry was picked out by Fowler as the soldier with whom he was on 7 December, and who was present in the taxi cab on the night of the murder of Hailstone. He was also picked out by Constance Jennings and Francis Michael Wettner (known as

Freddie) as one of several American coloured soldiers who stayed
at their house on the night of 6 December 1943, and *not* 7
December as stated by Leatherberry.

On 18 December, which was ten days after murder, I took
measurements of the fingers of both men, which were also photographed. This was done with their consent and I also scraped all
their nails.

The measurements were as follows:

George Fowler :   1. Right thumb nail: .65 inches (pointed).
                      2. Left thumb nail: .70 inches (rounded).
J. C. Leatherberry : 1. Right thumb nail: .70 inches (rounded).
                      2. Left thumb nail: .60 inches (rounded).

It is of interest in view of these measurements that Fowler is a
left-handed man. Examination of the material from under the
nails of the two men was carried out by Dr Davidson and was
reported as follows:

(*a*) *Fowler :*   1. Right hand: 2nd and 5th fingers
                        —blue fibres.
                    2. Left hand: 2nd and 4th fingers
                        —blue fibres.
(*b*) *Leatherberry :* 1. Right hand: Blue and pink fibres
                        under the 1st finger. Blue fibres
                        under 2nd, 3rd and 5th fingers.

These fibres were similar to those found on the jacket of Hailstone and also those from the fingers of Hailstone. Human blood
was found under the nail of the 3rd finger of the left hand of
Fowler—and *under all the nails of both hands* of Leatherberry.

The enquiry was completed by a statement from a woman
called Harvey of Umberstone Street, Stepney, who said that she
was with a coloured soldier with a tooth missing on the night of
6 December but *did not see him on the night of 7 December.*
A check on Leatherberry's statement that he spent the night of
7 December with Huntley and Harris at 'Freddie's' house also
showed that it was in point of fact 6 December; this was confirmed by a soldier called Harrison who was also there. Further,

E

Huntley's stay at Rowton House was confirmed by the porter there, who was quite certain that Leatherberry was not there at the time. Finally, enquiries at the Camp regarding the return of Leatherberry and Fowler showed that Fowler entered Hut 14 at midnight of 7 December with another soldier who was not recognised and that they remained for about five minutes and left together. Nobody saw Leatherberry in the Camp until midday on 8 December when he was spoken to by an officer and asked to account for his absence from Camp since 5 December, to which he had replied, 'I got drunk at Maldon and did not know my whereabouts', this contradicting his statement that he got back at 1 p.m. by bus. Unfortunately finger prints taken from the car were not satisfactory.

On this evidence the two men were handed over to the custody of their Commanding Officer and were both charged with the murder of Hailstone whilst Fowler was also charged with larceny. The case for the prosecution was that the motive was robbery conceived by the two men during the journey from London.

Fowler and Leatherberry were tried separately by American Courts Martial, with two coloured officers on each court, at Ipswich on 19 January 1944, and both pleaded 'Not guilty'.

The case against Fowler was based upon the statement made by him which contained information that only somebody present at the time could have known. This was supported by the identification by Captain Weber of the man and the property that had been stolen from him. Supporting evidence was the false alibi and the scrapings from the finger nails. Leatherberry was called to give evidence against him but merely said that he knew nothing about the matter at all as he was not there; but Fowler, in the witness box, repeated his own statement in support of a defence that he had nothing to do with the actual murder. At 11 p.m. that night Fowler was found guilty of murder by the court and was sentenced to life imprisonment and forfeiture of all civil rights with dishonourable discharge.

Leatherberry, against whom Fowler gave evidence, which included a demonstration upon his defending counsel of the strangulation hold, put forward a defence of an alibi supported by some girls from the Minories, one of whom explained the blood stained pants by contamination by her menstrual blood. This, however, failed by reason of the groups of all the girls being other than Group AB and also their failure to recognise the pants. The case for the prosecution was based upon Fowler's statement together with the nail scrapings and the false alibi and he was convicted by a majority of the court of murder and by a unanimous court sentenced to death by hanging. He was executed at Shepton Mallet, and confessed ten days before the execution, stating that Fowler had actually killed Hailstone. It is of interest to speculate who was the leader and who actually did it.

I have nothing further to add other than to say that any one of us who had the opportunity of seeing 5,000 coloured American troops in one camp can only be filled with admiration for Detective Superintendent Totterdell and his assistants for their courage in tackling such a problem and their persistence and hard work in bringing it into the list of solved crimes.

5 The Mummy of Rhyl

THIS case was the last in which the late Sir Sydney Smith was actively involved. As it was impossible to establish, directly or indirectly, a cause of death by violence, and as the clinical history was consistent with death from a natural disease (disseminated sclerosis) from which the dead woman had suffered, the accused was acquitted of murder and instead convicted of fraud.

THE PATHOLOGICAL INVESTIGATION
E. Gerald Evans

Rhyl is a popular seaside resort on the North Wales coast. Near to the railway station there is a row of terraced houses known as West Kinmel Street, and Number 35 was occupied by Mrs Sarah Jane Harvey, a widow aged sixty-five. She had lived there for many years, and had from time to time taken in paying guests.

At the beginning of May 1960, Mrs Harvey was admitted to hospital for investigations, and her married son decided to decorate the house during her absence. There was a hall leading to a staircase and two downstairs rooms, whilst at the top of the stairs was a landing with a large wooden cupboard which had been locked for many years.

On 5 May 1960, Mr Harvey in the course of his decorations opened this cupboard, and as a result consulted the police later that day. At 11 p.m. I arrived at the house, and was later joined by Dr Alan Clift of the Biological Department of the North Western Forensic Science Laboratory, Preston.

The cupboard proved to be made of pinewood, measuring externally 7ft in height, 3ft 9in in width and 1ft 5in in depth, and above it was a vent which opened into a loft. The back and left-hand side of the cupboard were formed by the landing wall, and the bottom consisted of the wooden floor of the landing. A fly-paper was suspended from a hook at the top of the cupboard and was covered with flies while numerous cobwebs clung to the wall and dead spiders adhered to them. The wallpaper on the back was dry and in good condition. On the left-hand side of the floor was a rounded object covered by a mass of cobwebs, mould, brown dust and pupa cases, in the centre was a portion of cloth material, and in the right-hand corner a brown human foot was visible, and gentle brushing aside of the dust and cobwebs showed the rounded object to be a human face. Further investigations were hampered by the cupboard being fixed, and any manoeuvres inside were accompanied by clouds of thick, choking dust. The available light shone from behind the investigators and produced consequent shadows.

It was decided to remove the material covering the floor, which consisted of a blanket which was very friable and came away piece-meal, and in the folds was a second flypaper covered with moths which were later identified as the clothes moth. Beneath the blanket was a folded bedspread tightly packed between the thighs, and portions were also found on the chest, covering a blue dressing-gown which covered the whole of the body from the neck to the knees where it was knotted in front. Beneath the dressing-gown there was a nightdress with a V-shaped neck. All these articles of clothing were friable, adherent and tore badly.

These operations exposed the body of a mummified person. The skin was rock hard and limbs could not be moved. On inspection with a hand lens a piece of coiled string-like material 2in in length was found on the left-hand side of the neck. The right-hand side of the neck was hidden by a rotated and flexed head. The thighs and knees of the body were found to be in a flexed position, the right forearm lay across the chest and the left arm was extended at the side of the body. As the body was adherent to a piece of linoleum which covered the cupboard floor boards, a garden spade was used to lever it on the linoleum out of the cupboard and the position of the linoleum in relation to it was noted before they were separated with some difficulty. The mummy remained rigid, and a further inspection outside the cupboard did not reveal other portions of material on the neck. It was then removed to the mortuary and a further examination carried out in good lighting (see p132).

The skin of the scalp and face was brown or black in colour. The remainder of the body was yellow-brown except in the breast region, where it was light yellow in colour, and distinct breast contours could be seen. By using firm pressure, pitting of the scalp and face could be obtained, but the rest of the body was granite-like in consistency. The skin was peppered with maggot holes, and a distinct grooving of the skin at the base of the left ring finger was present. The ears were small and shapely. Black sclerotic sacs were present in both orbits. The tongue was missing. The teeth were absent, and the gum margins smooth. The nostrils were dilated, the mouth opened and lips distorted. The eyebrows and eyelashes were missing, axillary hair was absent, but a few pubic hairs could be identified. The hair of the scalp was reduced to a stubble 1 to 3 millimetres in length, and microscopic examination showed that these hairs had clean-cut edges. Forbes (1942)[1], investigating the death of two premature infants found in a mummified state, pointed out that the larvae of the brown house moth attacks skin, hair and internal organs. Subsequent experiments in this case showed that the larvae of the clothes moth may eat keratin and produce the clean-cut appearance of the scalp hair found on the mummy.

The dust and mould which was adherent to the skin of the neck was brushed away from the exposed portions, revealing a

distinct groove on the left side of the neck, running from a localised depression at the front slightly upwards to become continuous with a groove at the back. It measured 1.5 centimetres in
width and 0.5 centimetres in depth except at the angle of the
jaw, where it broadened to 2 centimetres in width. The localised
depression at the front of the neck was elliptical in shape and
measured 2 centimetres by 1.5 centimetres by 0.5 centimetres.
At the base of this depression there was a series of six longitudinal
grooves. Having observed the depression on the left-hand side,
the mummy was tilted on to its left side to give as clear a view
as possible of the right-hand side of the neck. As this was done,
a brown tape-like object was found hanging from the back of the
neck adjacent to the groove formed by the chin pressing against
the shoulder. This fell away, and inspection of the groove
showed a further piece of material emerging from it. A finger was
inserted into the groove and the material which appeared to be
adherent to the skin of the neck could be teased from its position
in the fold. As it came away it was found to have a knot at its
front end. The outer surface of the material was grey in colour,
but it was thrown into folds, and on opening the folds it was
found to be brown in colour and resembled stocking material.
The knot was a tightly tied reef knot. It was noticed that when-
ever this material was placed on the table it formed an arc.
After photographing it was dispatched to the Forensic Science
Laboratory at Preston.

An X-ray examination showed closure of the epiphyses, a
female shaped pelvis, early osteo-arthritic changes in the sacroilac
joints and calcification of the costal cartilages, which suggested
it was the body of a middle-aged female. No fractures, no metallic
foreign bodies and no foetal parts were noted.

At 4 p.m. on May 6, the mummy was placed in a bath and
immersed in a 15 per cent solution of glycerine. Although mummified material in small pieces has been softened by using sodium
carbonate (Ruffer (1921)[2] and Sandison (1955)[3] used a solution
of alcohol, formalin and sodium carbonate), in order not to com-

plicate subsequent chemical analysis, glycerine only was used. Frequent examinations were made, and by 10.30 a.m. on May 8 the skin of the mummy had softened sufficiently for an internal examination. The hips and knees were extended with difficulty and the skin at the back of the knees tore badly. The height was estimated at 5ft 4in.

Post-mortem Examination

1. *The head*   No bruising of the soft tissues of the scalp was found. The skull showed no fractures. Suture union was erratic, but suggested middle age. A marked degree of hyperostosis frontalis was present, and the pituitary fossa was slightly flattened. The dura was easily recognisable lying on the base of the skull, but no brain tissue was present.

2. *The neck*   It was now possible to rotate the head to its normal position, but because of the danger of tearing the neck skin the body was not turned over in order to photograph the back of the neck. With the head straightened it was found that the grooving on the left-hand side of the neck continued across the front of the neck to join a deep tunnel on the right-hand side. The base of the tunnel measured 1.5 centimetres in width and the skin was smooth. It was noted that the depression on the left-hand side of the neck was considerably shallower after immersion in glycerine. The skin of the neck was removed as a collar. This exposed the hyoid bone, epiglottis, thyroid cartilage and six tracheal rings. With the head in the midline, the local depression of the skin of the neck corresponded with the left lamina of the thyroid cartilage which was depressed below the level of the right lamina and showed a groove. The muscles of the neck were represented as friable cords of tissue. The great vessels of the neck were absent. The hyoid bone, the epiglottis, the thyroid cartilage and the tracheal rings were placed in 10 per cent Kaiserling solution.

The hyoid bone and thyroid cartilage were X-rayed and no fractures found. The superior and inferior cornu of the thyroid cartilage were reasonably flexible, but patchily calcified on X-ray examination.

3. *The chest* The costal cartilages were calcified and there were no fractures present. On deflecting the skin of the chest, a few fibrous cords represented the intercostal muscles. The thoracic cavity was empty apart from two small portions of lung tissue which were dry and brittle. Between these there was a mass of adipocere to which recognisable cordae tendinae were attached. The diaphragm was intact but paper-thin and friable.

4. *The abdomen* A thin strip of liver tissue was adherent to the inferior surface of the right diaphragm. The stomach, small intestine, ascending and transverse colon were absent, although 5in of descending colon were present in which there was solid faecal material. Culture of this material, both aerobic and anaerobic, grew no organisms. The pancreas, spleen and kidneys were absent, although in the region of the left kidney there was a mass of adipocere. The uterus, cervix and vagina were missing, but there was a small fragment of bladder wall behind the pubis.

5. *The periphery* Dissection of the legs and arms revealed thin, fibrous muscle cords, well preserved tendons and interosseus membrane, but no recognisable blood vessels or nerve tissue could be found.

After fixation of lung tissues and larynx in Kaiserling Number 1 solution they were placed in 95 per cent alcohol and carefully observed at regular intervals over a period of three hours. No haemorrhages appeared on the surface of the pleurae, but a few small black dots rapidly appeared on the surface of the epiglottis. These were examined under a plate microscope, but they showed as amorphous, slightly raised nodules which did not suggest a haemorrhagic phenomenon, and at a later date semi-serial sections showed no erythrocytes or haemosiderin.

An excellent survey of the histological techniques used in the study of mummified material was given by Sandison (1955).[3] He recommends a softening fluid consisting of 96 per cent ethyl alcohol, 30 vol; 1 per cent aqueous formalin, 50 vol; 5 per cent

aqueous sodium carbonate, 20 vol. This is allowed to act overnight. The tissue is transferred to 80 per cent alcohol followed
by 8 per cent phenol in alcohol, absolute alcohol, three changes
of amyl acetate, three changes of 1 per cent celloidin in methyl
benzoate and then through benzene embedding into paraffin.
This method was used for subcutaneous tissue in the limbs, much
of which had remained brittle and hard after dissection of the
mummy. Sodium carbonate solution as recommended by Ruffer
(1921)[2] was used to soften portions of skin which had remained
firm after immersion in glycerine. Such tissue rapidly softened
and could be dehydrated, cleared and embedded in the usual
way.

The neck skin was cut into many pieces during the course of
investigation and was stored in 10 per cent formal saline. Professor Harrison of The Department of Anatomy at Liverpool University kindly let me remove a portion of thigh skin from an
Egyptian mummy (late dynasty, approximately 500 B.C.). This
tissue was hard and Sandison's technique was used in preparation
of paraffin control sections. Various portions of skin stained by
haematoxylin and eosin showed occasional islets of epithelium,
but most of the epithelial layer was represented by amorphous
material only. Hair follicles were easily recognised in scalp
sections. Muscle and collagen were differentiated by Van
Geison's and Mallory's stain, but attempts to demonstrate muscle
striation using phosphotungstic haematoxylin and alcoholic
Celestin Blue failed. Cartilage was seen in the walls of the bronchi
but the lungs showed fibrous septa only. Sections of the adipocere attached to the cordae tendinae showed a small coronary
vessel quite clearly. The liver stained as an amorphous mass with
no recognisable cell structure.

Numerous sections of the epiglottis and neck skin were examined for the presence of red blood cells and were stained by the
eosin-phloxine-tartrazine method of Lendrum, Van Geison's
stain and phosphotungstic acid haematoxylin. Small round bodies
staining deeply with Orange G were found in many sections of

the neck skin. Sandison found structures in the thyroid gland of mummified material which demonstrated the appearances and tinctorial reactions of the erythrocytes, and these measured 3.5μ as compared with 4μ in control material. Wilder (1904)[4] claimed to have stained erythrocytes which measured only 1.9μ in diameter. The presence of clearly identifiable erythrocytes was not noted in the tissues of the neck, apart from one section stained by eosin-phloxine-tartrazine, where a capillary containing erythrocytes could be clearly seen. Pearl's iron stain used in sections from the epiglottis and neck skin (and many were examined) showed no haemosiderin.

Anatomical Investigations

Following the autopsy examination the mummy was disarticulated and the remaining flesh removed from the limbs by soaking in a warm, weak solution of sodium carbonate, followed by treatment with a scrubbing brush. The skeleton was transferred to the Department of Anatomy at Liverpool University, where Professor Harrison carried out a detailed investigation of the bony structures. During the course of his examination Professor Harrison consulted Dr G. A. Harrison, Lecturer in Anthropology, Professor Farmer of the Liverpool Dental Hospital and Dr H. H. Francis of the Obstetric Department of the University. I have chosen extracts from a most comprehensive report.

(a) The human remains were those of a European woman, aged forty to sixty. It was not possible to estimate the age with greater accuracy, as the hyperostosis of the frontal bone produced discrepant findings in the closure of certain sutures of the skull.

(b) The appearances of the skull and lower jaw suggested that the teeth had been extracted many years before death—probably as much as twenty years—because of the lack of alveolar ridge in the mandible and the sharp alveolar margin of the maxilla. The obliquity of the angle of the mandible suggested middle age, and the lack of prominence of the masseter attachment on the mandible, a female sex. The prominence of the myelohyoid ridge and the height of the mental foramen suggested an age between fifty and sixty-five years.

(c) Estimation of height according to the formula of Dupertuis and Hadden (1951),[5] which included measurements of the right femur, tibia, humerus and radius, gave an average range of 161.75-162.21cm.—A mean average of 161.98cm or 63.82in (range 63.73in to 63.91in).

Estimation of height according to the formula of Trotter and Gleser (1952)[6] included the measurements of the right fibula and ulna as well as the bones mentioned in the previous formula. This gave an average range of 156.79-164.43cm or a mean average of 160.61cm or 63.28in (range 61.77in to 64.38in). These measurements show accurate approximation when both formulae are compared.

(d) The pelvis was narrower than normal in the intercostal, interspinous and external antero-posterior diameter. This suggested an android pelvis. Measurements of the true pelvis demonstrated that although the antero-posterior diameter of the pelvis was actually greater than normal, the antero-posterior diameter of the cavity and outlet appeared markedly less than normal. This suggested not only an android pelvis, but also that the deceased was kyphotic.

From these observations it was thought probable that the deceased would be unable to bear children without the aid of a Caesarean section.

(e) The left tibia was much less radio opaque than the right, suggesting a greater degree of osteoporosis in the left tibia than in the right. At the lower end of both tibia, lines of arrested growth were obvious on X-rays. These findings suggested first, that the deceased used her left leg less extensively than the right, and also that the deceased may have had illnesses or administration of medicines containing arsenic, lead or iron at the age of fourteen to sixteen.

(f) The bones of the right side were better developed and

longer than those on the left side, suggesting that the deceased person was right handed.

During investigations Mrs Harvey had told the police of a Mrs Frances Knight who came to board with her in the early weeks of the war. Mrs Knight was a semi-invalid and could not walk properly. A few weeks after Mrs Knight's arrival Mrs Harvey heard her screaming. She found her on the floor in a nightdress and coat, complaining of severe pain. Mrs Harvey went downstairs to make a cup of tea and on her return she found her dead. She was alone in the house and was scared. She dragged the body to the cupboard and locked it. She did not tell anyone that Mrs Knight had died, and in order to keep things going she collected money due to Mrs Knight as a result of a court order.

Investigations into the medical history of Mrs Knight showed that she suffered from disseminated sclerosis, and was last seen at a Liverpool hospital in December 1939.

Blood Grouping of Mummy

A sample of mummy tissue was dissected out after the mummy had been softened in glycerine. This was dispatched to Dr Madeleine Smith, Palaeoserologist of the Sub-Department of Anthropology, British Museum. Dr Madeleine Smith sent samples of this tissue and control material to the Department of Clinical Pathology, The Charing Cross Hospital Medical School, for examination for bacterial contamination. The following organisms were found to be present:

Streptococcus faecalis; Clostridium sporogenes; Clostridium histolyticum; Clostridium tetani.

No yeasts or fungi were present.

As adipocere was found to be present, and as Mant (1950)[7] found that Clostridium Welchii was conducive to the formation of adipocere, it is interesting to note its absence in this case. Stack and Morgan (1949)[8] showed that enzymes from Clostridium Welchii may cause degeneration of group specific substances. It was also interesting to note that in spite of the widely differing methods of preservation and greater opportunity for bacterial activity in the mummy, all the organisms present in the mummy and control material were identical. The method of testing in this case by Dr Madeleine Smith was based on that used by Boyd and Boyd (1934-1937)[9] on archaeological material and aged mummified tissue.

Dr Madeleine Smith concluded that the genotype of the mummy could have been A_1B or A_2B. Samples of blood were taken from two sisters of Mrs Knight and two nephews of Mrs Knight and these were examined by Professor Harrison and Dr G. A. Harrison. The two sisters were Group A_2 and one nephew Group O. Dr Madeleine Smith concluded that from this evidence an A_2 gene and O gene were present in the parent generation; either could be inherited by Mrs Knight. It is highly probable that she would have inherited an A_2 gene. There are four genes within the ABO group which have to be accounted for in the parents. Amongst the probable genotypes it has to be considered that one of the parents could have been heterozygous BO. It is also possible, but not probable, that one parent may have carried an A_1 gene. The results obtained in blood grouping the mummy would be consistent with the view that the body was that of Mrs Knight.

Conclusions

Mummification It would appear that the mummification of Mrs Knight was a natural process. The doors of the cupboard would allow a free access of air, and in this case a gradual process of drying must have occurred. Chemical analysis of the mummified tissue showed no poisonous substances.

The disappearance of the internal organs may be attributed to the action of fly larvae, and the disappearance of the hair to the larvae of the clothes moth.

Cause of death Post-mortem examination and histological examination failed to establish a cause of death.

The stocking The portion of stocking found in close proximity to the neck, and the foot and welt of the stocking adherent to the linoleum, were considered by Dr Clift to be part of the same stocking, and that the shape and stitch count of the portion in contact with the neck skin suggested that the stocking had been used as a ligature.

An interesting point concerning the stocking and its contact with the skin of the neck arose during the course of the investigations. Portions of the neck skin were looked at on many occasions between May and October 1960. At the beginning of October the portions of neck skin were on the histology dissecting board, and up to that time no suggestion of pattern marks had been found. On this occasion I was called to the telephone and returned after a period of ten minutes. By this time the skin had dried, and on one small portion I found a criss-cross pattern mark about 0.5 centimetres square. This was immediately photographed and later examined by Dr Clift, and at a later date this was examined by the defence experts and mentioned in court. Since then I have been informed that soaking portions of skin in phenol may reveal a hidden pattern. At any rate it would appear therefore that when examining material which has undergone a degree of putrefaction, drying it after fixation in formalin may be a helpful procedure.

Post-mortem I had been unable to ascertain whether the stocking had been placed round the neck before or after death. There was no histological evidence to suggest a tight application of the stocking during life, but that the stocking may have been applied tightly was inferred by Dr Clift's examination of the material, which had an estimated circumference of 11in. My findings of a deep groove, a localised depression on the front of the neck and the flattening of the left lamina of the thyroid cartilage was suggestive of a tight stocking round the neck. I considered that the reef knot was of no value in differentiating between possible suicide or homicide, and an article by Simpson (1960)[10] showed that in his experience a reef knot could well be suicidal.

Mrs Harvey was charged with the murder of Mrs Knight and committed to stand trial at the Ruthin Assizes 1960. Leading for the prosecution was the Solicitor-General, Sir Jocelyn Simon, QC, MP, assisted by Mr Elwyn Jones, QC, MP, and Mr Bertrand Richards. Mrs Harvey was defended by Mr Andrew Rankin, assisted by Mr Somerset Jones. The points of defence are outlined in the next article.

REFERENCES

1 Forbes, Gilbert (1942). *The Police Journal*, Vol XV, No 2.
2 Ruffer, M. A. (1921). *Studies in the Paleopathology of Egypt*. Ed, Moodie, R. L., University of Chicago Press.
3 Sandison, A. T. (1955). *Stain Technology* 30, 277-83.
4 Wilder, H. H. (1904). 'The Restoration of Dry Tissues with especial reference to Human Remains.' *Am. Anthrop* 6, 1-17.
5 Dupertuis, C. W. and Hadden, J. A., Jnr (1951). *Am. Journal of Physical Anthropology* 9, 15.
6 Trotter, M. and Gleser, G. (1952). *Am. Journal of Physical Anthropology* 10, 463.
7 Mant, K. A. (1950). London Univ M.D. Thesis.
8 Stack, M. V. and Morgan, W. T. J. (1949). *Brit J. Exp Path* 30, 470-83.
9 Boyd, W. C. and Boyd, L. G. (1934). *J. Immunol* 26, 489.
  Boyd, W. C. and Boyd, L. G. (1937). *J. Immunol* 32, 307.
10 Simpson, Keith (1960). *Int Crim Pol Review* 15, 138, 137.

THE DEFENCE
Francis E. Camps

Unfortunately for scientific observation but for reasons that are otherwise obvious, full reports of murder trials in which there is an acquittal are rarely published. The case of *Regina v Harvey* fully deserves reporting because, owing to the meticulous care taken by Dr Evans in his investigation of the body of Mrs Knight, much useful scientific knowledge has been acquired. As will be seen, in addition to the title of 'the Mummy case' might be added 'bricks without straw'.

Dr Evans has already dealt with the result of the detailed examination of the body and of the scientific observations made by Dr Clift. It was after these findings had been given in evidence at the magistrates' court that Sir Sydney Smith and myself were asked to advise the defence and in doing so we were given every facility by the Director of Public Prosecutions and by Dr Evans.

The following is a summary of the case for the prosecution: (1) the body found in the cupboard was Mrs Knight; (2) she had died of strangulation by a ligature (stocking); (3) at the hands of Mrs Harvey who had subsequently concealed the body in the cupboard for many years until it was finally discovered by her son on 5 May 1960 whilst decorating the house during her absence in hospital.

The defence also had the assistance of Sir Francis Walshe on the neurological aspects of Mrs Knight's illness, and Mr Jones of the Laboratory of the Manchester Chamber of Commerce.

Advice was sought on the following points:

(1)   Could identification of the body as Mrs Knight be upset?
(2)   What proof was there that she *died* of violence?
(3)   What proof was there that she did *not* die of natural disease?

The description of the body as given by Dr Evans immediately called to mind Figure 89 in *Forensic Medicine* by Professor Keith Simpson which shows the body of a newborn infant with a stocking tied around the neck with a caption below which states 'the ties afford only presumptive evidence of a criminal act for there is nothing to show the infant was alive or that asphyxia ensued'. This is not entirely comparable with the case of Mrs Knight, for proof that death was caused by strangulation by the ligature is complicated by whether it was born alive, yet in both cases, although the findings may give rise to grave suspicion, in neither can it be said on objective scientific grounds that the ligature caused death. This is by no means a unique situation.

In the case of Mrs Knight, without proof that it caused her death, three possible explanations for the presence of the stocking existed, which are: it was applied after death; or was applied in life to kill her; or was applied in life and had nothing to do with her death.

As scrutiny of the findings of Dr Evans showed quite clearly,
F

no internal organs were present other than some dried fragments which were obviously of no assistance in establishing the cause or mode of death. The whole case for the prosecution from the medical point of view therefore rested upon the condition of the stocking tied around the neck and the groove mark caused by it, for there was no scientific proof it was placed there in life. In spite of this the defence was placed in the position of having to prove that it did not cause death or perhaps, if that is putting it too high, might not have caused death. There were two ways to do this:

(1) by showing that death could have been due to natural causes;

(2) by showing that the stocking might not have been applied for strangulation.

(1) From the point of view of the first proposition as stated by Dr Evans, the medical history of Mrs Knight showed that she had been a patient of Lord Cohen in Liverpool and that he had made a diagnosis of disseminated sclerosis. To support this, there was, in addition to correspondence between her own doctor and Lord Cohen, the hospital records which were available. There was also some evidence to suggest deterioration in her neurological condition.

In this connection Sir Francis Walshe pointed out that the position of the body in the cupboard as shown in the photographs was typical of the late stage of disseminated sclerosis. Death in such circumstances would most likely occur from an intercurrent infection or possibly ascending infection of the kidneys. There was, however, no evidence of urinary infection. He also said that, from a clinical point of view, persons suffering from disseminated sclerosis may deteriorate very rapidly. This view was agreed in evidence by Lord Cohen himself when he was called by the prosecution to prove certain documents. There existed, therefore, more than a possibility that she had died of natural disease.

It was decided that there would be no value in challenging the identification of the body as that of Mrs Knight.

(2) The groove mark around the neck was physically associated with parts of a material which appeared to have caused it.
On the assumption that this was a stocking, could there be an
innocent explanation for its presence?

Attention was drawn during the trial to an old custom, *not*
limited to the North of England, of tying a stocking or sock
(preferably unwashed after use) around the neck when ill, and
that this was true was obvious from an immediate exchange of
glances in court when it was first mentioned. Further, the con-
gestive type of death which is seen in self-strangulation will
tighten further a ligature so as to produce not only a mark but
also petechiae above the level. Thus, there *could* be an innocent
explanation for the presence of the stocking.

Now the incorrect use of a word may well lead to false assump-
tions, and in this case the so-called mummy was not a true
mummy but a shell of dried skin and bones with some adipocere
formation. The explanation of the cause of the mummification as
being from exposure to draught was also somewhat over-
simplified, yet from the point of view of impact on the minds of
the jury it seemed to satisfy them as to what might have happened. Yet it is not uncommon to see in any coroner's area the
bodies of people who have not been found until several days,
weeks or even months have elapsed after death. These cases
afford excellent information of the process of decomposition at
different stages under different indoor conditions and in the case
of Mrs Knight the evidence suggested that following death the
usual process of putrefaction took place and with it the deposition
of the eggs of flies which eventually hatched and the larvae
devoured most of the soft tissues. At the same time the skin
slowly dried producing a 'cast' of the position of the ligature.
The stocking would become fixed by decomposition products and
as in the early stages of decomposition of tissues wet gas formation would cause the neck to swell, even a loose tie around it
would tighten sufficiently to cause a depression, and as the drying
process took place the stocking would remain on it, reproducing

the pattern by contact with the sodden desquamating skin. Dr Evans has described the reappearance of the pattern and was present when it was observed. Sir Sydney found in his collection of photographs some excellent examples of similar 'grooves' produced under various conditions, the best being on the leg in a case of drowning. It is of interest that since the trial I was shown in the Museum of the Medico-Legal Institute in Vienna a similar groove and pattern on the back of the neck of a body which had been there for many years.

The explanation of the depression on the front of the neck which overlay the left lamina of the thyroid cartilage with its overlying pattern as being due to the knot would obviously be attractive but was contradicted by the knot being found at the side of the neck, and no explanation as to how it could have got there was really satisfactory.

In his evidence Dr Evans quite properly said that the actual cause of death was unascertainable from his examination. This was stressed by the judge when he later agreed that the murder charge should be abandoned. After Dr Evans had completed his evidence, the only matter that remained was whether the stocking had or had not been tightly stretched.

It was to a great extent the basis of the case against Mrs Harvey in the magistrates' court that there was proof that it had been stretched. This, however, was not 'tested' by cross-examination until the trial, when it was even then not completed owing to the illness of the witness.

To summarise the defence claimed to show on evidence

(1) That there was an alternative explanation for the presence of the stocking around the neck other than strangulation.

(2) That the appearances found by Dr Evans might be produced by the process of post-mortem changes.

(3) That it was possible that Mrs Knight might have died of natural disease.

(4) That there was no evidence of stretching of the stocking other than by ordinary wear and tear.

Conclusion

The trial came to an abrupt end on the fifth day. The Solicitor-General made a submission to Mr Justice Davies that he thought it would be wrong to invite the jury to bring in a verdict of guilty of murder. The judge concurred and said that the prosecution were in no position to prove whether the stocking had been stretched. A formal verdict of 'Not guilty' was returned by the jury. Mrs Harvey pleaded 'Guilty' of falsely obtaining £2 a week from the Clerk to the Justices of Prestatyn between 1-3 May 1940 and 21-23 April 1960, by pretending that Mrs Knight was alive. She was sentenced to fifteen months' imprisonment.

6   Unexpected Death

Blessed is the man who expects nothing,
For he shall never be disappointed.

THIS quotation may well offer the clue to the detection of unsuspected homicide; for the alternative words for unexpected,
such as 'sudden' and 'unforeseen', do not have quite the same
meaning. A death which may be expected to take place can still
be of unexpected causation. It is for this reason that any fallacy
in thinking, such as an acceptance of the obvious or a lack of true
critical approach, alternatively known as 'taking the easy way',
may well become closely allied to self-deception and lead to
humiliation.

Thus, when told of the death of a patient who was known to be
seriously ill and not expected to survive, it is rare for the practitioner to scrutinise the mode of death in the absence of the
possibility of cremation, especially if he is not present at the time.
In fact it is open to doubt whether, if it did not fit into the expected pattern, this fact would outweigh any already preconceived
idea. This very conception may be criticised on the basis of
demanding too much introspection, but in fact no medical practitioner receives much encouragement to think on these lines for
he is not even required by law to see the body after death. He
therefore can scarcely be blamed for missing an unnatural death

and giving an incorrect cause, when he can equally well have certified as dead the wrong person. Alternatively, there have been occasions when the 'deceased' person was not even dead. Unfortunately, such errors, which may be excusable if the body has not been seen, also occur on occasions when an examination has taken place. Thus, it was not very long ago when a doctor was called to the house of a local clergyman whose wife was lying dead in bed. As he had not seen her for some time he quite properly informed the coroner and at the same time said he was prepared to furnish a death certificate for coronary thrombosis. An autopsy, however, showed the classical findings of carbon monoxide poisoning, which was confirmed by chemical examination of the blood. The husband, when questioned, admitted that he had found his wife with her head in the gas oven, but as she was 'a good woman', had placed her in bed before sending for the doctor. The husband's conduct was the subject of some comment at the inquest, at which the doctor was not present. It is possible that had he been there, he might well have taken refuge behind the fact that he was not a 'police surgeon'. Yet it is the likes of him who are the first line of defence against the unsuspected, unnatural death. This was well illustrated in the case of Teahan (R. v Quinlan CCC, 1962), which is discussed in Chapter 9.

The basic approach to this problem was put most realistically by a well known American analytical chemist (toxicologist) who said that he was tired of hearing his colleagues recount at meetings the number of cases from which they had isolated poisons during the previous year. He felt that it would be of greater value to know the number in which they did not know what to look for before commencing the analysis, and in how many they were left with a substance which they were unable to identify. The same applies to violent deaths for it does not require much medical knowledge to appreciate that a body with seven chopper wounds on the head gives rise to 'grounds for suspicion' of foul play. Then, provided the examiner either has experience of forensic medicine or is in a position to call upon the services of someone who has, the investigation should present little difficulty apart from any confusion at the scene of the crime which may be caused by the usual mêlée of specialists such as photographers and fingerprint experts. There may also be competition between the non-medically qualified forensic scientists, the pathologists and the police surgeons, whilst of course there is the ever-present danger of treating it as 'an ordinary domestic murder', which nearly always means some lack of care. On the other hand, should somebody unexpectedly drop down dead it will be the surrounding circumstances which should direct attention to the possibility of suspicion. It is surprising, nevertheless, that even then things can go wrong, as in a case in New York City when an assistant medical examiner, called to the sudden death of the proprietor of a shop, gave a certificate for a natural death due to 'coronary artery insufficiency' after he was told that the man had on occasions complained of praecordial pain and was under a doctor for coronary artery disease. From the moment he received this information, he did no further examination—an omission he later regretted when an exhumation revealed that the man had been shot.

Such stories are rather more common than is appreciated, and probably the classic example was in the case when Thompson was stabbed by Bywaters in the road. The body was taken to the mortuary after a doctor had pronounced life extinct; there it was undressed, revealing a stab wound in the back, which was interpreted by the police officer as 'It must have been where the doctor tested to see if he was dead'. Some years later in the same district a local practitioner was called to see a man dead in a room with large quantities of blood splashed all over the place. He promptly pronounced life extinct and (having heard the man had tuberculosis) gave the cause of death as haemoptysis. At the mortuary seven knife wounds were found. These are only two of many examples of accepting the obvious; amongst others is that of a woman who was found dead with her head in the gas oven—the doctor who was called said it was a case of coal-gas poisoning, a 'diagnosis' which was not challenged by the police sergeant, for after all, who was he to disagree with a doctor? Death was later found to be due to strangulation, the most apparent sign of which was a ligature mark around the neck.

It is very easy to be critical, but few can look back without recalling similar errors, perhaps mercifully of less consequence and by no means limited to the medical profession. Thus a woman was found dead in the back yard of a house in Hampstead, both naked and having obviously been the centre of no mean conflagration. Closer examination showed a groove on the neck, unaffected by the fire, with a cut in the skin caused by removal of a ligature, which proved to be a scarf, parts of which were found nearby and in a waste-bin. A senior police officer quite seriously suggested that it must be a case of suicide; and when asked to explain the scarf ligature suggested, 'She must have had a sore throat.' Such an approach is usually associated with a subconscious desire for an easy solution, either from idleness or, as in this case, 'annual leave'. It is not always completely divorced from fear of looking a fool. (R. v Christophi CCC, 1954. See p46.)

Self deception may sometimes be in part due to forming a preconceived idea, and it is for that reason I myself am reluctant to perform an autopsy with too much prior knowledge. It is unfortunately only too easy to find what one expects, even to the extent of missing the obvious, especially when dealing with conditions in which the post-mortem findings are minimal such as in deaths due to coronary artery insufficiency. I have a suspicion that a similar attitude may well lead to miscarriage of justice once objectivity is lost. Thus it could occur in charges under the Road Traffic Act, for it is difficult to escape the thought that the smell of drink in the breath is not entirely dissociated from the monotonously repetitive evidence which is given so often by the police in such cases: 'His breath smelt strongly—his eyes were bloodshot and glassy—his tongue was furred—he staggered heavily—his speech was slurred'—an inco-ordination which scarcely fits in with the same person having dropped his keys, stooped down without fumbling, picked them up and locked the door of the car in semi-darkness. Nor does it seem inconceivable that anyone who has been called from his warm bed on a cold night, having been told by the police that he is to examine a man who is 'intoxicated', might start off subconsciously prejudiced, a state of mind which might not be diminished by questions directed to earlier movements of the suspect and how much he has had to drink. Such information may be of assistance in adding confidence to a decision, but it is, nevertheless, difficult to understand how it will assist in forming an opinion as to impairment in ability to drive—the first thing to be established—which one would think would be better derived from objective tests. Nor is it of great value in arriving at the second point—the cause of the impairment—as the Road Safety Act 1967 requires scientific measurement of blood or urine alcohol levels in cases of suspected drinking and driving. It may be that the reason for the questions is more subtle and is to prove the suspect a liar as to the amount he has drunk. In a criminal case it might well be contrary to the Judges' Rules.

Failure to see the obvious occurs at the highest levels, as was well shown in the case of the Piltdown Man. A more difficult and dangerous situation is not that of missing the obvious but of accepting the obvious. An example of this is seen in the case of Watters, whose death was accepted as suicide for more than a year after he was found hanging in the REME Barracks at Duisburg.

Just as all cases of hanging are not suicide, so too, of course, patients do not always die for the reason expected. Sometimes this may be because something else, such as coronary thrombosis, intervenes in the terminal stages of a fatal and painful illness. No one can doubt that this is a merciful intervention when it is a pathological process, but when due to human interference— whether for sympathy, the advancement of science or just greed —it is abnormal and, however well intentioned, liable to misuse.

Thus, to most of us who are sufficiently God fearing and law abiding, although the idea of deliberately hurrying Aunt Agatha's last few days on earth might be distasteful, if faced with subjecting her to a painful end, we might feel an overdose justifiable. Ethically, of course, it depends upon whether the overdose was to relieve the pain (whilst appreciating a calculated risk) or to kill her. Therein lies a fine ethical point. So too, the removal of the kidney of an unconscious person who is believed to be certain to die may well appear superficially justifiable. Nevertheless, if it hastens the death it is legally homicide. Undue haste in stopping the respiration as soon as the object is achieved is also homicide and might be considered less excusable (or tactful) than if a decent period were allowed to elapse before doing so. It should be pointed out that in the case of an overdose, it is a matter for the conscience of the administrator, but in the other it is known to the observers.

There are circumstances in which pathological knowledge co-exists with lack of legal experience so that at autopsy the observation of the conditions from which the person was suffering is divorced from the cause of death. A simple and not too serious example is seen in hospital post-mortem rooms where the disease processes are carefully demonstrated without any real appreciation or thought as to why the patient died or the implications thereof. Thus it is not uncommon for pulmonary emboli (obstruction of an artery in a lung by a blood clot) to occur following head injuries: from a strictly legal approach, with the high standard of proof required in a criminal case, this is not due to the head injury—with the lower standard of proof in civil cases, it is. So too, it is not generally known that many citizens, especially in the USA, carry a double indemnity life insurance policy which means that twice as much is paid if the death is due to an accident. Failure to distinguish between the cause of death and the disease from which the person was suffering may well influence the future financial comfort of the dependant. Hence a sudden death in a slowly dying person is always worth careful consideration, as indeed is the terminal event in a chronically ill person. In the same way, the assumption that a person who has died of poisoning has committed suicide is not always correct, and the truth that it was an accident, even if it does not financially benefit the relatives, may well relieve their minds, for even in this outwardly realistic world convention still exists.

Finally, there is the question of the difference between proof and suspicion. This is very real, and again I refer to the difference between civil and criminal cases. In the 'Mummy' case suspicion was high and proof was low.

I have attempted to put forward the hypotheses that in these days of scientific knowledge the public and the courts should expect scientific standards in which evidence should be capable of scrutiny and testing of the same standard as would occur in the academic world. To quote Maier Tuchler, a leading American forensic psychiatrist, 'There is in addition to self deception and even error, a danger that information may become arrogant misinformation even in the best hands and with the best of motives'. To this I would add that the danger should be guarded against by self criticism and, above all, by preventing 'science' becoming synonymous with 'pseudo science'.

7 Attempted Death by Electrocution

EVERY YEAR about forty people in England and Wales lose their lives by electrocution in the home. Too often there is evidence of unsatisfactory wiring carried out by an amateur to effect replacements or improvements. Other common causes of accident are neglect to obtain competent advice following 'little shocks' from appliances, failure to repair damaged or worn insulation, and attempts to carry out repairs without turning off the main switch.

The minimum current to kill from electrocution is stated to be about 65 milliamperes. Death from electricity can occur in two ways, either by a sudden shock causing vagal inhibition or by true electrocution which produces ventricular fibrillation or respiratory failure. Although the importance of the element of surprise should not be over-emphasised, cases have been recorded in which death has occurred from touching a wire which was believed to be live but which was, in fact, dead.

From a practical point of view, it should be stressed that to receive the full effect it is necessary for a good 'contact' to exist with 'live' point and with 'earth'. Dry human skin is a poor conductor with an average resistance of 2,000-3,000 ohms but when it is wet the skin resistance is reduced to as little as 500 ohms. If the skin is punctured the effective resistance will be that of the subcutaneous tissue, which always has very much lower resistance than the skin. A current of about 12 milliamperes may make it impossible for a person to release his grip upon the 'live object' if adequate earth is present. Other modifying factors will be the duration of exposure and the area of contact, whilst it is possible that the actual voltage received may be less than that computed because of electrical leakage.

It is a popular idea that water is a good conductor and that therefore a person is more vulnerable to electrocution when immersed in a bath. This is not always the case, for during the investigation of the case of R. v Whybrow, which is mentioned later, experiments showed that a person sitting in that particular bath was, in fact, insulated. The bath itself is not the true reason for the bathroom being one of the two most electrically dangerous rooms in the house (the other is the kitchen), the risk lies in the damp atmosphere when associated with a large number of metal objects (mostly well earthed) such as the water taps and pipes. For this reason it is necessary either to instal the electric switches outside the bathroom, or, if inside, to operate them with a pendant pull-cord of non-conductive material. In spite of this, safety precautions are rendered quite valueless by the introduction of some portable electrical apparatus such as an electric fire, a hair dryer, an electric kettle or even a wireless set. All, if properly constructed and intelligently used, are safe enough, but unfortunately they have often been made unsafe by unskilled wiring or rough handling. It is therefore no great surprise to hear of deaths from electrocution caused by the handling of electric appliances when seated in a bath.

When accidents occur, it is not uncommon for the electrical expert to find that an electric kettle or heater has been amateurishly rewired with omission of an earth lead, which makes it inevitable that, in the presence of a fault rendering the casing alive, any person handling it will take the full force of the current.

One early morning a husband heard a thud in the kitchen to which his wife had gone to make a cup of tea. He got up at once and found his wife lying dead upon the kitchen floor. She had apparently been electrocuted from the casing of an electric kettle. This was confirmed by electric burns on the thumb and finger, whilst earth had occurred from her arm being in contact with one of the metal objects in the kitchen. The plug was examined by an expert electrician who found:

(1) There was no earth wire connected.

(2) That the person who had wired up the plug had left sufficient loose wire to flap over and short on to the case.

Even a properly wired kettle may be dangerous if handled by an ignorant person, as the following case will illustrate:

An elderly woman went out of her house one afternoon and forgot to switch off her electric kettle. This boiled dry during her absence and the safety mechanism blew out the plug, making it impossible for her to replace the plug after refilling the kettle. Under the impression that there was 'something stuck' she took the plug in one hand, thereby earthing herself with the earth safety metal strip upon it, and with the other hand introduced a metal screw driver into the positive terminal which was still connected to a 25-ampere power plug at 'on'; she somewhat naturally received the full charge with fatal results.

Careless maintenance of electrical equipment may well result in death and it is most surprising that many housewives of more than average intelligence will continue to use vacuum cleaners whose flex is bare from constant wear and tear. Similar accidents occur with electric lawn mowers.

Two other kinds of domestic electrical equipment deserve mention—radio and television sets. These have been the cause of fatalities and afford an excellent example of the casual manner adopted by the public towards electricity. How often has a person been heard to say, 'A funny thing happened this morning. I got a shock off my radio,' and when asked what had been done about it, given the reply, 'Nothing'? Education of the public to take notice of small shocks and call in an expert electrician would pay dividends.

Children, having small fingers, may be electrocuted by poking them into the holes of the standard plug or alternatively using metal objects such as skewers or knives. The close proximity of excellent earths such as gas pipes makes this even more dangerous. The risk can be reduced by fitting plugs with safety shutters. An example of this type of accident occurred some years ago under the following circumstances.

A child aged five years was playing in a hall closet. Suddenly it collapsed and a doctor who was called found it to be dead. Detailed examination showed electric burns on the tips of the right index and middle fingers, one of which had a round depressed area. The post-mortem findings internally were consistent with electrocution. Examination of the closet showed a porcelain fuse box with bare wires sunk into the top in gutters too small to allow access of an adult finger but large enough to admit that of a child's finger. The bare end of the wire exactly fitted the depression on the child's finger and evidence showed that the child had been standing bare-footed upon a gas pipe when collapse took place.

Other fatal accidents have occurred from children climbing up and touching overhead cables, and on one occasion a boy scaled a pylon for the purpose of throwing two metal cups tied together over the cables carrying the grid across the Thames. A blinding flash was seen for some miles and the body of the culprit was found at the base of the pylon with a broken neck and extensive electrical flash burns resembling crocodile skin down the whole of one side of his body. A case was recently recorded of a child electrocuting itself by chewing through a length of electric flex.

As I have said, death from electrocution may be due either to ventricular fibrillation or respiratory failure; unfortunately, in neither case are the post-mortem appearances peculiar to the effect of passage of an electric current, for they are quite commonly seen, for example, in deaths resulting from coronary insufficiency or cerebro-vascular catastrophes. The proof that electrocution is the cause of death must depend upon the identification of an electric burn. This demands a careful scrutiny of the body surface of *everyone* who dies in close proximity to any electric live point.

The appearance of an electric burn has been described as a hard blister with a central 'white parchment' bleached area and a hyperaemic zone of surrounding skin. The identification and interpretation of this lesion may not be easy and there is also considerable doubt as to whether such an appearance may not also be produced by exposure to an electric current shortly after death. The actual appearance of the electric lesions will vary according to the firmness of the contact. Thus, if the contact is poor in pressure and area, there will be small pricked-out 'spark burns'. If a diffuse area is involved with moderately firm application there may be a shaped burn which after a few hours may even show charring, especially with high voltage currents. The exit lesion may be less obvious and not so characteristic. In true electrocution, burns may be completely absent, and it should be borne in mind that this may occur where a person is grasping an object, such as a pistol-grip drill, at the time it becomes live. Electric burns are usually more extensive than their appearance suggests, and later considerable sloughing may occur. Histologically an appearance has been described of elongation of the basal cells and nuclei but unfortunately this is by no means consistent and can occur from thermal burns.

Probably most domestic deaths are due to ventricular fibrillation, and the post-mortem appearances closely resemble those due to coronary artery insufficiency. Those due to respiratory failure will show more pulmonary oedema and certainly occur when the current passes through the medulla oblongata.

Suicide by electrocution is uncommon and such cases as occur are, as might be expected, somewhat bizarre in character. On one occasion death was brought about by preparing a circuit from the domestic supply using rings on a finger of each hand to connect to a plug, whilst in another a complicated electrode was placed over the praecordium (the left side of the chest, behind which the heart is located), the circuit being closed by a wire

G

from the same plug being held in one hand.

The use of electricity for homicide is believed to be very rare but it may be that cases have passed unrecognised owing to lack of identification or even search for electric burns. The following case illustrates an attempt at murder, and scrutiny of it will show how easily it could have been missed if the woman had died and no suspicion had existed.

R. v. Whybrow (Essex Assizes 1952)

The accused was a married man living with his wife and children near Southend-on-Sea. One evening his wife decided to take a bath and whilst she was doing this, he was in a bedroom on the other side of the passage. Suddenly she cried out, saying that she had received an electric shock when she had touched the soap dish. After a short interval he went to the bathroom and, decrying the suggestion of a shock, touched the soap dish to show that she was mistaken. At the time she was satisfied with his statement but the next morning decided to telephone the Electricity Company to ask them to call and examine the soap dish. They were too busy to do this immediately and consequently she decided to examine it herself with the aid of her sister-in-law. After scraping away the plaster she found that it was fixed to the wall and that there was a wire to the bracket which had been made from a piece of tin by her husband. She traced the wire under the bath (boxed in) through the wall into the adjoining lavatory, where, after winding around the base of the lavatory pedestal, it entered the roof space above and then ran across the top to a cupboard in the bedroom where it was connected to a metal tube secured between two pieces of bakelite which were screwed to the wall. She then called the police who carried out a search and in a drawer found a length of india-rubber-covered electric wire, one end of which was attached to the positive terminal of a 15 ampere plug and the other to a large split pin which exactly fitted the metal tube in the cupboard. In the circuit had been introduced a 15 watt bulb with holder. A 15 ampere power-plug was fixed on the skirting board adjoining the cupboard and the whole circuit when connected allowed a current of 65 milli-amperes to be detected at the soap dish (the reduction was due to the resistance of the bulb). Examination of the bath showed that a person seated in it would be completely insulated. This was due to the porcelain being intact, the runaway being insulated by the plaster which fixed it, leaving the only earth through the chain attached to the bath plug. An appreciable electric shock could be felt when the soap dish was touched.

Investigation showed that the husband was associating with a young girl without telling her parents that he was already married. His wife had discovered and resented this liaison. He had moreover been previously convicted of bigamy. His defence was that the apparatus was the earth of his wireless set but the jury found him guilty of attempted murder.

Conclusion

To summarise, the recognition of death from electrocution is not easy unless the medical practitioner who first sees the case is both suspicious in his approach and careful in his examination of the body. In two fatal cases, although the possibility of electrocution was considered and discarded at the time, this was not detected until some weeks later. In neither case was anything to suggest electrocution shown by autopsy and no local burns were present.

Examination of cases of electrocution which have occurred each year shows the main reason for the accidents is faulty wiring installed by amateurs.

8 Carbon Monoxide Poisoning

SINCE 1950, when this paper was written, there has been a drastic reduction in the number of deaths caused by domestic gas. This is to a great extent owing to the education of the public and the efforts of the Gas Boards. The introduction of non-poisonous 'natural' gas has resulted in a further important drop.

Of all poisons, carbon monoxide offers the greatest opportunity for accidental or improper use. Happily it is usually part of a mixture (coal gas) with a characteristic smell which is associated in the minds of the public with danger, but when it is present in a form not easily recognisable then it becomes a menace both to the community and individual.

I propose to limit myself to the commonest form in which it occurs, namely coal gas or, as Americans call it more graphically, illuminating gas. In this form the characteristic smell advertises its presence so long as the person has a sense of smell. As it is piped under pressure, the hissing sound which usually accompanies its escape gives a warning provided there is acuity of hearing. The unfortunate person who has neither sense of smell nor hearing is, however, completely at its mercy, and this applies especially to the aged.

In order to appreciate the poison it is essential to know its properties. The normal composition of coal gas is about 5-22 per cent of carbon monoxide and this gas possesses about 300 times as great an affinity for haemoglobin as oxygen. A relatively small percentage of the gas in the air can build up quite a high percentage in the blood, given sufficient time. It affects human beings because, when the haemoglobin is combined with carbon monoxide, it cannot then take up oxygen, and consequently if the blood level of saturation rises above a certain figure an individual will suffer from oxygen deprivation. Approximate figures are as follows:

At 20% saturation there are symptoms if the body is being exercised.

At 30% symptoms at rest.

At 40% severe symptoms, eg inco-ordination—staggering, and

At 50-70% unconsciousness and death.

This is dealt with most comprehensively by F. E. Mills, BSc, MInstGas E, AMIChemE, and F. C. Smith, FCS, MInstGas E, in a paper to London and Southern Gas Association on 12 May 1950, North Thames Gas Board. As is always the case with human beings there must be considerable variation. Hence a person with poor blood supply to the heart muscle, such as occurs in coronary artery disease, may well die more easily, and a person with heart failure, in which there is already a poor oxygen exchange between the tissues and the blood, if deprived of further oxygen will undoubtedly have symptoms earlier than a normal person. In the same way, with a moderately high saturation it may be possible to walk some little way starting from rest but with additional exercise death may occur. With this basic data may I draw your attention to problems with which we are confronted.

The first question is the initial identification of coal gas poisoning and in most cases this is based upon the smell of gas and the presence of a gas point with the tap turned on. In an 'uncomplicated' case the amount of smell will depend upon whether the supply is main or meter. In the former, escape will persist until turned off, whilst in the latter the volume will depend upon the amount remaining to be exhausted and the smell, though usually persistent, may disappear.

The second factor is the honesty of the person discovering the incident who usually notifies the police. Cases may be misleading owing to the assumption that because there is gas the death is due to gas poisoning. The following case illustrates the danger of jumping to conclusions. A small child ran into a neighbouring flat and said that her mother and father were asleep on the floor of the kitchen and she could not wake them up. The man and his wife were found lying upon a mattress in front of the kitchen gas cooker, the door of which was open and the burners full on. A police officer was called and ordered their immediate removal to hospital, where they were both certified as dead from coal gas poisoning. This illusion persisted until a post-mortem examination upon the wife showed marks on the neck and haemorrhages into the eyelids and skin of the face, indicating that she had died of manual strangulation. There was no carbon monoxide in her blood whilst her husband's blood showed a full lethal saturation.

When the relatives wish to avoid a suicide verdict, and turn off the gas and remove the body to another room or different surroundings, the initial investigation becomes most difficult for an unsuspicious or inexperienced person. There may be only the appearance of the body upon which to rely and not infrequently it is viewed in a poorly lit room or by the aid of artificial light. The following case illustrates this. A man was reported to the police as having died suddenly, it being merely stated that he had been found collapsed. At autopsy the characteristic appearances of carbon monoxide poisoning were found with a blood saturation of 70 per cent and no natural disease. After considerable interrogation it was ascertained that in fact the man had been found in the kitchen near the gas oven with the unlit burners full on. The relatives were afraid of a verdict of suicide which they felt would invalidate a life assurance policy, and they had taken precautions to avoid it.

This was deliberate concealment and deceived both the police and the doctor called at the time. Faked stories of symptoms of heart disease have been produced by people of intelligence or cunning. Sometimes the situation may occur when a doctor who is expecting his patient to die is informed of his sudden death and automatically issues a death certificate. A doctor was called urgently to see a patient, a man of 63, whom he had last seen 12 days before suffering from inoperable carcinoma of the stomach. He found him lying dead upon his bed and was told that he had collapsed. The doctor issued a death certificate which was not accepted by the Registrar because the relatives complained that the man had been found on the floor near a gas ring which was turned on. At post-mortem, apart from slight pink colouration of the hypostasis, nothing was obvious externally, but examination of the blood showed 50 per cent saturation with carbon monoxide. An inoperable carcinoma was present. It is clear that the doctor did not suspect carbon monoxide poisoning, and if the relatives had not complained, the man might have been buried as a case of natural death.

These may seem exceptional cases, but there are possibly many others, especially in areas where the Coroner foregoes post-mortem examinations, and they serve as a warning of the risk of missing cases of less innocent association.

Circumstantial Evidence

It is a forensic axiom that cases fall into three categories, *suicide*, *accident*, or *murder*, and usually in coal gas poisoning they are sieved in this order by the police. In this particular type of death it would appear better to reverse the order, and this would make the primary investigation more thorough. Dr Keith Simpson has kindly let me have his total figures of deaths from carbon monoxide poisoning:

Suicide 746; Accidental 87; Homicide 5—Total 838.

Thus gas offers itself as an easily accessible method of suicide and is available for an impulsive act, especially for the lonely housewife. The commonest places chosen are the kitchen and the bedroom, using the gas cooker, gas fire or supply from a gas point with tubing for convenience. The identifying details, apart from a note or possibly a psychological background, are sealing of the windows and cracks of the doors. In many cases there is obstruction of the chimney, and a position of reasonable comfort of the suicide with a pillow for the head. The trays in the gas cooker are usually removed and the doors of the room are frequently locked on the inside. Such cases do not usually present any difficulty, although Dr Keith Simpson has seen a case of coal gas poisoning with the dead person's head in a gas oven and a bruise on the head, which proved to be a case of murder. Sometimes the person may be found dead at a distance from the gas point or even in another room. This may be explained by a change of mind at the last moment, and collapse due to the effort in the presence of fairly high saturation with carbon monoxide. Occasionally a suicide uses apparatus such as a gas mask under which is led a tube, or covers the head with a mackintosh or blanket in the form of a tent. I have also seen the gas pipe sawn through on the supply side of the meter.

A large proportion of these cases are clear cut, but the absence of a note, sealing of the doors and windows or obvious preparation could indicate accident, although the background points to suicide. Such a verdict may be strenuously pressed by the relatives and the common suggestions put forward are accidental knocking on of a gas tap, or boiling over of a kettle. Such a thesis is difficult to disprove if the gas tap is accessible and not fitted with a safety device. The explanation of some of these border-line cases, especially in elderly people, is a confusional state in which the person turns on the tap and forgets having done it; with poor hearing and impaired sense of smell he or she is overpowered before realising what has happened. I have also had cases in which a partially closed tap has allowed a leak of gas into the room, and this has not been detected because of temporary loss of smell due to a cold. If hearing is normal and a sense of smell exists accidental escapes should be easily detected, but partial combustion of a faulty portable stove may well lead to a fatal dose. Fatalities from the boiling over of saucepans and kettles are nearly always associated with some temporary incapacity due to illness. One uncommon form of accidental carbon monoxide poisoning arises from leakage from cracked pipes. This was seen during the blitz, and it is said that seepage through the ground will remove the smell. I saw a rather unusual example of this type just before the Normandy invasion. The Southend arterial road was being used as a vehicle concentration area for army vehicles and they were parked on the greensward with the drivers sleeping beside them. Two Canadian soldiers who were sleeping under a ground sheet could not be roused one morning and one of them whose head was under the sheet was found to be dead, with a lethal saturation in the blood of carbon monoxide. The other later recovered consciousness in hospital. Investigation showed that a gas main under the grass verge had fractured from the weight of the vehicles (which it was never designed to take) and seepage had occurred.

Rare cases of accidental death are seen when a suicide, without thinking of the safety of others, gases himself, and the gas, passing into another part of the house, kills somebody who is asleep at the time.

A most interesting case, which is almost an invitation to intelligent homicide, occurred in 1949. A young woman was 'picked up' at the lower end of Regent Street by two young American service men who took her back to a flat which they jointly rented in North London. They had separate bedrooms. The next morning one of the men got up, dressed and went out. Later the second man also departed, leaving the girl to clean up and, as they both thought, go home at her leisure. In the evening the first sailor returned and went into the kitchen and started to heat a kettle to make tea. Whilst the kettle was boiling the gas went out. He put another shilling in the slot and relit the gas, made his tea and went to bed in his room. His friend returned later and, on entering the flat, smelt gas. He went into his companion's room and found him asleep and semi-conscious. He then went into his own bedroom and found the girl in the bed with the gas fire fully turned on but unlit. She had died of carbon monoxide poisoning. It appeared at the subsequent inquest that the girl had gone to sleep with the gas fire on and that when the gas was exhausted, it had gone out. An escape of unlit gas occurred after renewal of the supply by the coin. Such a case requires careful early investigation by experienced CID officers.

Accidental death is not infrequent in the hanging and strangulation deaths of sexual perverts, but until about 1950 I had not seen coal gas used for the purpose of sexual stimulation. A smell of gas caused the police to enter a room and on the floor the occupant, a young man, was found dead, naked and covered by a mackintosh. Close to his hand was a rubber tube connected to a neighbouring gas point. He showed medical evidence of habitual sexual perversion (self conducted) and his wardrobe was filled with women's clothes. There was nothing to suggest suicide and the explanation seemed to be that whilst deliberately producing partial anoxia with the coal gas he built up a lethal saturation. These cases show that each presents a specific problem and they must be investigated with a very open mind.

Intentional

There now remain those cases associated with intent, and I have ventured to include the most controversial of them, the suicide pact. Here a conclusive decision is essential or an improper stigma may remain. I stress this because a person recovering from carbon monoxide poisoning may have a complete loss of memory for what has occurred, and it is always possible that what may appear to be a suicide pact may be, in fact, a combination of one person attempting suicide and the partner becoming accidentally overcome. Alternatively, the wife finding her husband dead may decide to commit suicide rather than live alone. A third possibility is, of course, the deliberate murder of one followed by suicide of the other. An elderly couple were found dead in a double bed from carbon monoxide poisoning. A piece of rubber tubing had been led from a neighbouring gas point to the side of the woman's face away from her husband. In this case several possibilities could be considered apart from suicide. The man might have deliberately placed the gas tube near his wife's face while she was asleep and laid down until he himself was overcome, or she might have done the same to him. Against a suicide pact was the position of the gas tube, which, it might reasonably be presumed, would be between them if there were a mutual arrangement. The answer must be purely speculative, as no assistance of any value could be obtained from such investigations as finger prints.

A case of suicide by the husband, followed by attempted suicide by the wife when finding him dead, was only solved by excellent police investigation. A smell of gas coming from a house resulted in its being entered by forcing the locked back door. In the living room a man was found dead on the floor with a stocking tied round his neck; this was not tight. There was a bruise on his brow. In the next room his wife was found unconscious with her head close to the gas oven whose burners were on and the trays removed. She was removed to hospital and later, owing to her confusional state, was certified. At first sight it appeared that she might have strangled her husband who was of poor physique, but careful investigation showed that a clothes hook behind the door had lost its lower screw, allowing it to swing sideways. The man had hanged himself on the hook and fallen following suspension, striking his head (which showed a bruise) against the door knob. His wife, returning and finding him dead, had attempted to commit suicide.

Coal gas offers an easy opportunity for faking a suicide after a murder has been committed, as the following case, crude as it is, well demonstrates. The neighbours in a flat above smelt gas coming from the ground floor rooms occupied by a woman who was separated from her husband. They found the woman with her

head resting in the gas cooker oven upon a greasy dripping pan
which had not been removed (an uncomfortable and dirty action
which is most uncommon with suicides). A local doctor who was
called stated life was extinct and due to coal gas poisoning. No
note was found. The police took no special action and the body
was removed to the local mortuary. The ambulance attendant
commented upon a mark upon the neck of the woman at the
mortuary, and later a post-mortem examination showed that death
was due to strangulation by the woman's blouse collar (black
moire silk ribbon). No carbon monoxide was present in the blood.
The husband who put forward an alibi was arrested and admitted
killing her and deliberately placing the head in the oven (it might
be argued to make quite sure she was dead). A verdict of manslaughter was achieved by the forensic skill of the learned counsel.
This is a good example of the danger of accepting appearances
on their face value. It is not uncommon for a person who has
committed a murder by violence to commit suicide by coal gas
poisoning which is the simplest method available. This is usually
done in a spirit of remorse to avoid the inevitable. The following
is an example of this. Nobody having been seen for four days in
a house occupied by a young married couple, the police forced an
entry and found the woman in the kitchen with severe head
injuries and covered by a blanket. Her husband was lying
in a position of rest close to the gas oven, with the burners on
and the tray out. The majority of the injuries on the woman had
clearly been caused by a wooden stool but there was also a bruised
laceration on the back of the head. Examination of their bedroom
upstairs showed blood staining of the pillow and also of a wooden
log in the fireplace. Downstairs a winged chair in the dining room
showed blood stains and a blood soiled towel was nearby. The
blood of the woman showed no carbon monoxide whilst the man
showed over 70 per cent saturation. With this assistance it was
reasonably easy to establish the sequence of events. The man
assaulted the woman in the bedroom with a log. After this she
succeeded in getting to the dining room, only to be assaulted

again with the stool in the kitchen. The man then committed suicide by coal gas poisoning. This shows the value of estimation of saturation in such cases.

The next example shows a somewhat similar case which at first sight appeared a possible 'outside job', and in which the solution was again assisted by the carbon monoxide saturation value of the blood. A man who lived in a flat with his elderly parents returned home during the morning and noticed a smell of gas. His mother was lying dead in bed without any signs of a struggle, whilst her pet pekingese dog was dead near the fireplace with two stab wounds in its chest. The kitchenette door was locked, and when it was forced the father was found lying dead on his back near the gas oven whose unlit burners were on and tray removed. He had incised wounds on the left wrist and tentative stab wounds on the chest. Reconstruction of the events was fairly easy in such a case, and was confirmed by the presence of 50 per cent saturation of carbon monoxide in the man. No carbon monoxide was in the woman (who had died of manual strangulation) or the dog (which had died of stabbing).

Infanticide (the killing of a child of less than one year and a day) by the mother and subsequent suicide constitutes, with suicide pacts, the commonest type of detected murder by carbon monoxide poisoning. Unfortunately, owing to the fact that children succumb more easily to carbon monoxide poisoning, the mother may survive and face a criminal charge.

The destruction of a child of 14, apparently without a struggle, is certainly most unusual. I saw the following case in 1949. A woman of about 46 years, happily married, but menopausal and with some background of mental disease, was found dead, lying across the bed of her daughter aged 14. The windows were shut and a rubber tube led across the landing to the woman's bedroom where it was connected to a gas point. There was no evidence of violence upon the child, and it seemed that during the night the woman had brought the gas tube into the room and held it near the child, later succumbing herself. It illustrates to some extent the fact that a person can be gassed whilst asleep without being aroused and without any preliminary narcosis or stunning. The difficulty here was to decide whether the mother poisoned herself at the same time or later, and the evidence pointed to the second explanation.

There is, of course, the type of case in which it is quite impossible to decide either who was the originator of a pact, if it was a pact, or exactly what did happen. Here is an example of such a case, resulting quite properly in an open verdict. A woman in the late menopause was found dead near the door of the bedroom which she shared with her young married daughter (whose husband was in hospital seriously ill). The daughter was lying in bed and there was a rolled up counterpane near her head. The mother's bed had not been slept in. A portable gas fire was 'on'. The chimney was blocked by a rug and the windows shut. Examination of the blood of the woman showed about 60 per cent saturation with carbon monoxide and that of the daughter a similar figure. No hypnotic was found on analysis in the organs of either body. Although the circumstances did suggest a suicide pact it was clearly impossible to obtain other than an open verdict.

The following is a case of exhibitionism (accidental carbon monoxide poisoning). A young man with a good academic career inherited some money and bought a house. He was found dead in his bed with the room full of gas which was still escaping from a pipe which had been sawn partially through with a hacksaw. The hacksaw was found in a drawer. The back door was unlocked. Investigation showed that he had attempted suicide on several occasions, each time being conveniently stopped in the nick of time. It appeared probable that he had staged the scene for somebody who failed to come at the expected moment, and was overcome by the gas.

Finally I come to an uncommon detected case of murder by coal gas. With many advantages, including a control, it was by no means 'water tight', because it was not investigated from the earliest moment. This, I submit, is the only way in which such cases will be detected. A woman (an epileptic) sent for a doctor and said her child aged two had suddenly collapsed and died in the main room of her flat. The doctor, one of the staff of a mission, felt instinctively that there was something wrong, suspected coal gas poisoning and informed the police. They called the deputy divisional police surgeon who, after examining the child, said dogmatically that death was due to natural causes. He was also asked to examine a baby aged about six months who was in a cot in the same room and said that there was nothing wrong with it. The police, lulled into a sense of false security by the medical opinion, made no further investigation other than the routine inquiries of a sudden death, and the body was removed to a public mortuary where I first saw it. There it lay along with a number of seasonal blue asphyxial deaths from chronic bronchitis, and its pink colouration stood out like a rising sun. Autopsy showed the characteristic signs of carbon monoxide poisoning with (as it was proved later) a saturation of over 50 per cent. In addition there was an area of oil soiling on the left side of the mouth, similar to the oil grease on the rubber pipe leading from the gas bracket to a portable gas fire. The baby acted as an excellent control. The woman adhered to her story, though no carbon monoxide escape could be found in the flat. She was charged with murder and was found unfit to plead at her trial at the Old Bailey. I think there is little doubt that the woman disconnected the tube and placed it in the child's mouth; there was more than adequate motive.

There is one aspect of all murders which must be appreciated, namely that because a person was already dying there is no reason to discard the possibility of murder. In fact, many dying people may offer a considerable motive for expediting their decease, and ill people, especially those with heart disease, not only die very easily of carbon monoxide poisoning but may show very little colouration.

How many deaths from carbon monoxide poisoning are not

identified, and how many of these are homicidal, are matters of conjecture. That gas is easily accessible and, in the absence of smell of the gas, may be difficult to detect there can be no doubt. It does seem, therefore, that the approach to such cases must be with more suspicion. The provision of some simple testing apparatus, such as that used in the RAF during the war in the cockpits of aeroplanes, employing a silica gel impregnated with potassium palladosulphite, could be helpful.

In presenting these cases, I have deliberately avoided an academic discussion on carbon monoxide poisoning with the intention of showing the unusual manner in which carbon monoxide poisoning may present itself in every-day practice of forensic pathology.

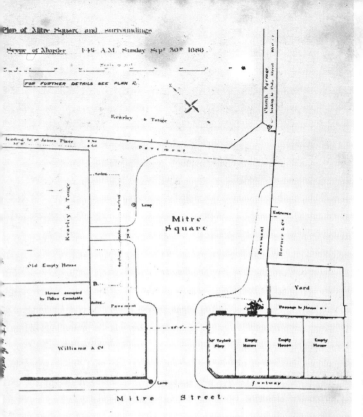

Plan of Mitre Square and surroundings

Scene of Murder 1.45 A.M. Sunday Sep.r 30th 1888.

FOR FURTHER DETAILS SEE PLAN B.

Kearley & Tonge

leading to St James Place

Pavement

Kearley & Tonge

Lamp

Mitre Square

Old Empty House

B.

House occupied
by Police Constable

Pavement

Williams & Cº

Church Passage leading to Duke Street

Entrance

Horner & Cº

Pavement

Yard

A

Passage to House

Mr Taylor's Shop

Empty House

Empty House

Empty House

Lamp

footway

Mitre Street.

Page 113
(*left*) Plan of Mitre
Square, scene of
the murder of
Catherine Eddowes
by Jack the Ripper

(*below*) Sketch of
Mitre Square
showing the
position of the
body. Taken from
point B on the
plan, looking
towards A

Page 114 (*above*) Position of the body of Catherine Eddowes when found. From a sketch made on the spot by Dr F. Gordon Brown; (*below*) diagram of the face of Catherine Eddowes, showing the principal cuts

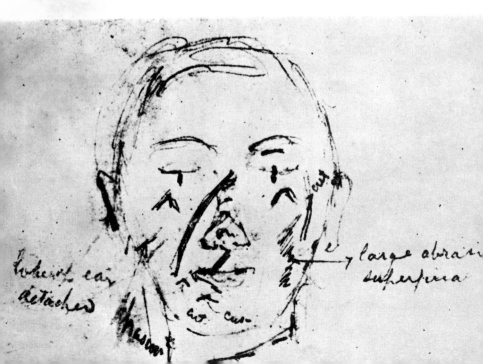

9 Alleged Murder by Household Gas

The high rate of detection, as recorded by criminal statistics, with respect to murder, relates only to those cases of death which have been successfully identified as homicides, and is, consequently, to some extent misleading. There are not a few cases in which it has been discovered that the body of a murdered person has been disposed of as though death had been due to natural causes (as a result of clearing up another murder). This suggests that many murderers must not infrequently succeed in avoiding the detection of their crime.

—Havard, *The Detection of Secret Homicide*

THE death of Michael Joseph Teahan, a young Irishman, occurred at 125 Andover Road, Holloway, a two-storeyed house owned by a Mrs Mary Kate Davitt. Her husband had died suddenly on 20 February 1962, and her son, Albert, then resigned from the Garda Siochana in order to come to England to look after her; both he and his mother occupied bedrooms on the ground-floor where there was also a front sitting-room. There were lodgers, all Irish—a man called Clifford, aged 20, who occupied the middle room on the first floor, and another called Swayne who had the back room, whilst sharing the front room was the some-

H

what odd combination of Teahan, aged 15, and a man called Quinlan, aged 51 years.

The story starts at 8 a.m. on 17 April, when Mrs Davitt got up, but it was not until about 12 noon that she went upstairs to clean the rooms and saw, through the glass window of the door of the front bedroom, the man Quinlan standing in the middle of the room apparently just getting out of bed. She was a little surprised at this, for he normally went to work early whilst his room-mate left at 8.30 a.m. Quinlan appeared to be wearing his shirt and was putting on his trousers whilst Teahan was still in bed, apparently asleep. She went downstairs again without opening the door, to give Quinlan time to dress; she did, however, notice that he had a stain on his shirt-sleeves. About 12.30 she again went upstairs; as she did not see anyone she opened the bedroom door, and a nasty smell assailed her nostrils—described at first as 'like vomit' and later as possibly excreta. She now saw Quinlan lying on his bed and said to him, 'Where's this awful smell coming from?' to which he replied, 'I have been sick, Mam'. Mrs Davitt then went over to Teahan's bed, not suspecting anything wrong, and said, 'Hello, Michael. Are you off for the day?' When he did not answer, she shook him and felt that his face and forehead were cold, whereupon she realised that he was dead. Naturally, she turned to Quinlan and told him this, to which he replied, 'He looks very white, Mam'—a somewhat surprising remark in view of the fact that he later said that he thought he was dead at 10 a.m.! As Mrs Davitt had still scarcely recovered from her husband's death, it is not surprising that, under the circumstances, she did not notice very much else but hurried out to tell her son who was at work at 4 Highbury Crescent. This she did at about 1 p.m. He revived her with a whisky at a nearby public house and telephoned the police at about 1.45 p.m. He then took his mother home, arriving at about 2 p.m., and went up to the bedroom where he saw young Teahan dead in bed, and noticed that there was no sign of disorder and no obvious smell except of excreta. Somewhat to his surprise, Quinlan was also in his bed and appeared to be asleep—even more surprising since his mother had told him that when she was there he was dressing. Davitt told Quinlan to get up as the police were coming, but he showed no inclination at first. Eventually, Quinlan got up and explained that the stain on his shirt was due to being sick during the night.

PC Taylor arrived at 2.10 p.m. and went with Davitt to the bedroom, by which time Quinlan was dressed in shirt and trousers. He was unshaven and there was dried vomit on the side of his mouth and also on his pillow. The two windows were closed and a gas-ring was in the 'off' position. In reply to his questions as to what had happened, Quinlan said that he had woken at 10 a.m. and was sick; at the same time he had spoken to the boy and got no answer. He said he did not know that Teahan was dead until Mrs Davitt told him. PC Taylor did not feel satisfied and went back to the police station, reporting the matter to the CID, and subsequently returned with the station sergeant and Detective Inspector O'Shea. Neither of them smelt anything other than stale beer and vomit on entering the room. Detective Inspector O'Shea spoke to Quinlan who said that he woke up at 10 a.m. and saw the boy 'holding a piece of paper to his mouth; [he] had spoken to him and got no answer'.

Considerable difficulty was experienced in getting a doctor and it was not until 3.20 p.m. that a Dr Cline arrived and certified life extinct, intimating that the cause of death was tuberculosis as there was some blood-stained froth coming from the mouth. He did notice that the hands were lying in a position suggesting that the body had been arranged, an observation subsequently rendered of little value at the trial when it was quite clear that the doctor's sight was not very good (he wore thick pebble spectacles and had to be guided up the staircase at the Old Bailey). In fact, Superintendent Millington, who was in charge of the investigation, felt that another examination should be carried out, and through the Coroner.

Dr Hugh Johnson, my senior assistant, went to the house with the police officers at 5.30 p.m. and from the colour of the body had no doubts at all that it was a case of carbon monoxide poisoning. He also made observations which led him to believe that death had taken place between 1 a.m. and 5 a.m. This was the first time that 'gas' entered the picture, and led to immediate examination for a possible source, which proved to be a gas-ring in the bedroom, the tap of which was in the 'off' position. This was supplied from a meter on the landing outside the bedroom where there was a 'cock' in the 'off' position. The gas supply was examined at 5.55 p.m. by a gas-fitter, who could find no leakage or defect but that the 'cock', which was operated by a square nut with a detachable spanner-type lever, was 'off' in a 'down' position instead of at right angles. Subsequently, it was found that a new meter had been fitted on 12 April when the cock was left 'on' in an 'up' right-angle position, ie the position in which it was found was down (off) but it should have been at right angles, as originally left. Hence, someone had altered the position of the handle. The meter was also examined and found to contain two separate shillings in the box, which was properly secured with a padlock; the supply of gas was exhausted. The meter supplied the three top bedrooms (gas-ring in the back room and gas-stove in the middle room) whilst a separate meter supplied the ground floor.

A post-mortem examination confirmed that death was due to carbon monoxide poisoning with a blood saturation of 74 per cent. In addition, there was evidence that the boy had recently been buggered (not for the first time) which was confirmed by examination of an anal swab.

This set in motion a full-scale investigation which revealed the following facts:

(1) Teahan, who was accustomed to having dinner at his brother-in-law's house about 25 minutes away, had been there for dinner at 7 to 7.30 p.m. and had left at 10.5 p.m. after watching the television.

(2) Clifford (middle room) returned to his room at 11.20 p.m. and did not see any light in the front bedroom but heard

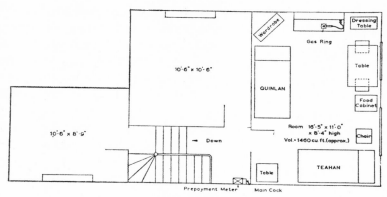

Fig 2   Plan of the Quinlan/Teahan room

someone talking. At 11.30 p.m. he went to boil some water but found there was no gas and so put 1s in the meter. This still failed to produce any gas—showing that at that time the gas was turned off at the main. He then went to bed.

(3)   He was awakened by a noise in the early morning—a noise as though someone was coming towards him and also someone snoring very loudly; later, he heard a number of 'bangs' coming from the front room. He was frightened and as his door was bolted on the inside, he hid under the bedclothes.

(4)   Swayne (back room) got home at 10.45 p.m., went to bed and heard nothing unusual in the night. He got up at 6.45 a.m. the next morning, tried to light the gas-ring in his room, found there was no gas and, as he had no shilling, gave up the unequal struggle and did *not* go near the meter. The last time he had put a shilling in the slot was on Saturday, 14 April.

(5)   From this it seemed clear that if Clifford had put a shilling in, on the night of the 16th, there must have been at least 72 cubic feet of gas used during the night by someone.

(6)   Clifford said he got up at 6 a.m., hurriedly dressed to go to

work and, as he left, he looked through the glass panel in the front-room door and saw a 'lump of bedclothes' in Teahan's bed. He did not use the gas in his room or smell gas *but* he did have a bad taste in his mouth in the morning, although he slept with the top of his window opened.

(7) The examination of the clothing of Quinlan and Teahan showed evidence which was sufficient to support that of the post-mortem examination: that Teahan had been the subject of buggery and that Quinlan could have been the other party; also that this must have occurred after Teahan got back. Clifford said he had heard suggestive noises on previous occasions.

There remained, therefore, Quinlan's own statements to consider; these cover some days but can be summarised as follows:

(1) His comments in the bedroom have already been given (3.10 p.m.).

(2) He was seen at Holloway Police Station at 4.50 p.m. when there was no suspicion of any offence. He said that, after leaving work on 16 April at 4.30 p.m., he went to a cinema in the Euston Road and remained there until 8.30 p.m. He then went to a nearby public house where he drank one pint of light ale and remained until 9 p.m. He then caught a train at Euston to Finsbury Park where he bought some fish and chips, which he ate on his way home, arriving at 9.30 p.m. He then sat in his bedroom writing a letter to a friend in America (at no time did he use the gas in the room). He said he was still writing when Teahan returned at about 10.30 p.m. After a short talk they each went to their own beds.

(3) On 18 April, when it was desired to interview Quinlan in view of the new situation that had arisen, he could not readily be found; but when he was, he was so intoxicated he spent the night at the police station (he had then been made to leave his lodgings by Mrs Davitt). He was quite unfit to make any statement.

(4) At 10 a.m. on 19 April he made the following statement:

(a) He saw Teahan first on 17 April at 10.10 a.m., which he fixed by having seen the time on Teahan's alarm clock.

(b) He then thought he was dead but just stayed in bed.

(c) He did nothing because it was an awful shock. He just went to sleep.

(d) At 12 noon he was seen out of bed by Mrs Davitt, and still did nothing.

(e) At 12.30, when told by Mrs Davitt that Teahan was dead, he did nothing.

(f) At 1.40 p.m., when Davitt came into the room, he was asleep again.

(g) He found the gas-tap in the bedroom off when he went to use it.

(h) No one came into the bedroom to his knowledge during the night.

To summarise, Quinlan said he did not know anything. However, when told about seminal stains on his clothes, he suddenly remembered that he had been with a woman on the way home on the night of 16 April and that must have been the source of the stains.

When told that he had never said it before, he said he didn't think.

At 2.15 p.m. on 20 April he was charged with buggery and, in reply, said, 'I have nothing to say now'.

On 21 April he appeared on remand at North London Magistrates' Court. Whilst in the cell passage he said—and repeated it again after caution: 'I now realise that it is best to tell the truth and I did commit the offence against the boy but up to now my mind has been hazy. I do want to say I can't remember turning on the gas and I want to beg forgiveness for what I have done.'

After he had signed it he said, 'I feel better in my mind now that I have told you that. I will send for you when I have thought about the gas part but before that I hope to see a priest'.

Quinlan was later charged with murder.

The Scientific Investigation

As things stood at this stage, there were certain aspects of the case which, to say the least, were puzzling. Thus it was quite clear that Teahan had died from carbon monoxide poisoning—presumably derived from household gas—and yet Quinlan, who claimed to have slept in the same room, had survived. So, too, although Clifford had put 1s in the meter, he was unable to light *his fire*, hence presumably the gas had been turned off at the meter—and yet, the next morning, although the gas was still turned off, the whole of the supply had been used. If the theoretical situation was correct, then Quinlan should know a great deal more than he had admitted. It was decided to request the assistance of Mr J. A. Prigg, a highly experienced scientist who was attached to Watson House, the research department of the North Thames Gas Board. He had assisted on occasions in the past, at the request of the coroner, in the investigation of cases of gas poisoning. On 25 April he went to the house, and his examination led him to believe that the gas-ring in the bedroom was the most likely source of the gas. The rate of flow from this was 22·3 cubic feet per hour whilst the amount of gas available for 1s was 72 cubic feet.

It was essential to ascertain the concentration of carbon monoxide at the heads of the beds and this was done by rubber tubes leading to the landing where samples were collected into bottles for analysis in the laboratory. The concentration of carbon monoxide at the two points was also checked by spot tests using the Draeger apparatus.

The results obtained were as follows:

	CO Percentages	
Minutes	*Teahan's Bed*	*Quinlan's Bed*
16	0·015	0·058
20	—	0·015★
32	0·054	0·103
40	0·08★	0·15★
46	0·086	0·153

Minutes	CO Percentages Teahan's Bed	Quinlan's Bed
71	0·118	0·181
75	0·10*	0·20*
102	0·138	0·156
105	0·10*	0·15*

*Spot tests

The results show that the concentration of carbon monoxide built up more quickly at the head of Quinlan's bed (ie, fatal in 1½ hrs for Quinlan; 2 hrs for Teahan). The equilibrium concentration of carbon monoxide in the room was 0·15 per cent, which is the equivalent of 68 per cent saturation (ie, as in Teahan's blood).

From the equilibrium concentration and the measured gas rate (22·4 cubic feet per hour) and carbon monoxide content of the house gas (14·4 per cent), it was estimated that the air changes

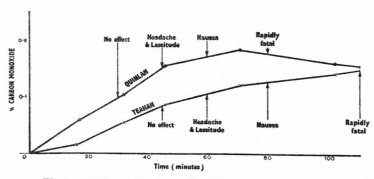

Fig 3   Build up of carbon monoxide during tests. Samples taken at bedheads

would be 1·5 per hour and, from this, the time taken for the smell of gas to disappear would be three hours after the tap was turned off. In most cases a smell will remain due to absorption into clothes or furnishings but in this case it was found that no smell persisted.

Certain variations had to be taken into consideration, including wind speed and temperature:

	Wind Speed	Temperature
On 17 April	Nil	44°F
On 25 April	6 - 8 knots from N.W.	65°F
On 25 May	15 - 18 knots from S.W.	

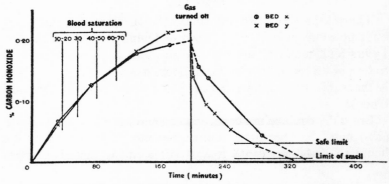

Fig 4   Build up and fall off of carbon monoxide at bedheads.
Tests 16 May 1962

From this it seemed likely that the concentration would have been higher on the night of Teahan's death.

In spite of what, to the non-scientists, might appear to have been adequate evidence, it was felt that, for a truly scientific standard, further data was essential in order to establish a case against Quinlan, which must depend upon proof of his absence from the room (ie, that if he had been in the room all the time, as he stated, he would have died). So, too, it was necessary to know what would have happened to the occupants of the other two rooms on the top floor and to anyone sitting on the landing.

A survey of the front bedroom had shown that there was a large gap at the top of the door and also that the windows fitted badly.

The tests on the landing were carried out at a height of 2-3ft from the floor.

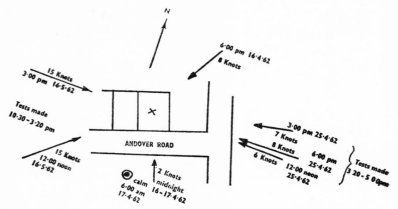

Fig 5 Wind plan

Tests on Landing

Time in Minutes	
0	Start of tests in the room
10	Smell of gas on the landing
30	0·008 per cent CO on landing
48	0·01　per cent CO on landing
80	0·01　per cent CO on landing

Further tests were carried out on 25 May :

The sampling points were set up as before and similar measurements taken, but after 198 minutes the gas was turned off at the main cock and the concentrations measured at the bed-heads and the landing.

Summary of Findings at 180 Minutes

Sampling Points	Concentration of Carbon Monoxide	Maximum Blood Saturation in Equilibrium
1. Landing (sitting)	0·030 per cent	30 per cent
2. Landing (standing)	0·030 per cent	30 per cent
3. Adjacent room (Clifford)	0·010 per cent	13 per cent
4. Half landing (Swayne)	0·006 per cent less	than 10 per cent

N.B. The estimated symptoms are based upon Henderson's Criterion which states: per cent concentrations of CO times time in hours equals 0·03.

Henderson's Criterion	Symptoms
0·03	No effect
0·06	Headache and lassitude
0·09	Nausea
0·15	Dangerous
Over 0·15	Rapidly fatal

From a practical point of view, it is said that the following is the relation of symptoms to blood saturation.

Blood Saturation	Symptoms
(1) 20 per cent	Symptoms at exercise
(2) 30 per cent	Symptoms at rest
(3) 50 per cent	Unconsciousness
(4) 60-70 per cent	Fatal

This must, however, be modified by the rapidity of the build-up and the activity of the person, as well as posture and whether disease process is present.

The findings on this occasion indicated:

(1)   The rate of the increase at the two bed-heads was the same as on 25 April (ie, a faster rate at Quinlan's than at Teahan's). Any difference is attributed to the wind speeds of 6-8 knots NE (Test 1) and 15-18 knots SW (Test 2).

(2)   It is estimated that the concentration of carbon monoxide would have fallen to a non-lethal level (ie, 0·03 per cent CO) after 300 minutes at Teahan's bed.

(3)   The limit of smell is based on a person coming from outside the room (ie, 0·03 per cent gas or 0·005 per cent CO).

(4)   The concentration in the adjacent room, landing and room on half-landing were as might be expected.

Conclusions:

On this scientific evidence, the results would mean—

(1)   Quinlan could not have been in the room all the time and survived.

(2)   Quinlan could have been on the landing and, if so, would have developed symptoms consistent with those described by himself.

(3)   Clifford could have developed slight symptoms, if he had been all night in his room.

Quinlan appeared at Old Street Magistrates' Court on 17 May 1962, where this somewhat complicated case was presented by Mr David Hopkins, and Quinlan was committed for trial at the Central Criminal Court on two charges, the first of murder, the second under the Sexual Offences Act 1956.

The trial on the first count took place on 20 June 1962, when Mr Mervyn Griffith Jones and Mr John Mathews appeared for the Prosecution whilst Mr Christmas Humphries, QC, represented Quinlan. Quinlan was ultimately acquitted of murder but, at a subsequent trial, was convicted of the charge under the Sexual Offences Act 1956.

I should like to revert to the relevance of the opening quotation from *The Detection of Secret Homicide*, and the suggestion made, not only by Dr Havard, but also in a report of the Forensic Medical Committee of the British Medical Association, which indicates the ease with which homicide can be concealed or missed.

10 The Bonnyman Case

MRS ELIZABETH BONNYMAN was admitted to hospital dying on 12 January 1942. She was then 37 years of age, the wife of Dr Bonnyman, a general practitioner whom she had married in 1930. She herself was a qualified nurse.

Her condition on admission was dreadful. She was emaciated, her weight being 3 stone 10lb whilst her height was 5ft 6in (normal weight 9 stone 10lb). She was clothed in pyjamas which were filthy and her body was covered in excreta, pus and dirt. The hair was matted and seething with lice. She appeared to be frightened, and apologised for her condition, saying: 'It is a month since I had any food, but I have had some drink.' The medical superintendent of the hospital was so horrified at the woman's condition that he rang up the police. An officer attended at the hospital and, after seeing her, interviewed Dr Bonnyman who was waiting in the passage outside the ward. He was dressed in rags, very dirty, unkempt, pale and emaciated.

The officer said to him: 'I have been told that you are this poor woman's husband. How did she get into this condition?' He replied: 'She would not let me do anything for her, she was very stubborn.' To this the officer replied: 'But it must have taken months for her to get into that condition and I am told you are a doctor.' Dr Bonnyman then said: 'Yes, I am a doctor. She has been ill since February but she wouldn't let me touch her and she wouldn't eat anything. She has had nothing to eat for six weeks.' When asked: 'Has she been taking drugs?' he replied:

'How did you know? She used to take drugs but she hasn't had any since August last year when I gave up my practice.'

Mrs Bonnyman in the meantime had said in answer to questions by the ward sister, that her husband lived with her and had neglected her terribly but had not ill-treated her, and that she would tell her all about it when she got better. She was in great pain and died the same evening.

A few minutes after her death her husband made a written statement to the police in which he said that shortly after their marriage his wife had become a morphine addict. He had tried to stop her but it had continued and she used to get the drug either from his surgery or from chemists. Constant addiction had weakened her constitution, and he detailed previous illnesses, some of which are described later. He attributed the abscesses on her body to the use of dirty needles and explained the state of poverty by the war and evacuation of the locality, which had ruined his practice and got him into debt. He said his wife for the last six weeks had sat in a chair and never moved and that she had been so weak that she had been supported by a soap box in front of her. She had been in constant pain and refused to go to bed because her back hurt her; she also refused solid food but drank milk occasionally. She had refused to let him look at her abscesses which, in his opinion, ought to have been lanced, nor would she let anyone else touch her or have another doctor.

A week before she died she asked him to put her to bed and he carried her upstairs. She was then wearing only a nightdress but her voice was strong and powerful until Saturday 10 January, after which he thought she was failing and determined to call in Dr Fenton; he postponed the call, at her request, until the Monday morning. In his opinion she must have died from septic absorption from the abscesses and malnutrition.

The death was reported to the Coroner and an autopsy was done the next day.

This showed, apart from the loss of flesh, excoriations and sores all over the body with pressure sores on the left hip, left thigh, bottom of back and left shoulder. Contractures of the right elbow (extension limited to 120°), both knees (left 90° and right 120°) and left elbow with swelling due to venous thrombosis secondary to a large abscess of the arm. There were further abscesses of the front of the right forearm, outer side of the right arm and front of the right thigh. These were situated in the proximity of hypodermic puncture marks which were easily identified by tattooing due to the needle having been coated with carbon. Their situation and direction was of some significance:

1. Outer side of the left thigh (downward direction).
2. Inner side of the front of the right thigh (downward direction).
3. Inner side of the left calf (upward direction).
4. Middle of the right calf (upward direction).
5. Outer side of the left arm (vertical).
6. Back of the right arm and forearm (vertical).
7. Lower abdomen.

The marks on the left thigh coincided with blue areas of bruising, suggesting that they had been caused recently. They were excised together with the subcutaneous tissue and sent for analysis. Bacteriological examination of the pus from the abscesses showed a variable flora, *Staph. pyogenes* and *Bact. coli*, being isolated from different sites, indicating different sources of infection. Scratch marks characteristic of production by finger nails and in keeping with self-infliction were present on the left side of the chest, whilst on the back were scars of old abscesses. A large subcutaneous abscess was present, extending from the right scapula to the sacrum and outwards to both iliac crests. Pus was draining, inadequately, through a pressure sore on the back and a culture grew: *Staph. pyogenes* (pure). No obvious puncture marks could be associated with this.

Internally there was no evidence of any wasting disease. The myocardium and the kidneys showed toxic changes and there was a terminal bronchopneumonia with one pyaemic (staphylococcal) abscess in the right lung. The liver showed toxic change and passive congestion whilst the spleen was enlarged and septic.

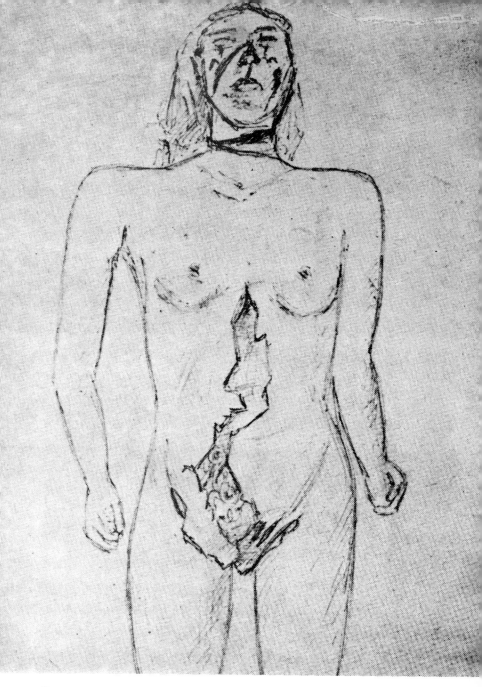

Page 131 Sketch of the body of Catherine Eddowes made at the mortuary by F. W. Foster

Page 132 (*above*) Untouched mummy, found in a cupboard in Rhyl;
(*below*) mummy in the mortuary ready for external examination

The conclusions drawn from the autopsy were:

1. The cause of death was bronchopneumonia due to a combination of undernourishment and multiple abscesses with probable chronic morphine poisoning.

2. There was evidence that for a considerable period the woman had been having hypodermic injections, the needles being coated with carbon particles. On occasions there had been improper sterilisation resulting in infection with abscess formation.

3. She did not appear to have had proper treatment for some period of time and absence of such treatment had contributed to her death. The treatment could only have been carried out in an institution.

Detective Inspector Rutherford, who was in charge of the investigation, visited the house where the Bonnymans had been living and took possession of a variety of objects including the following:

1. Some 12oz medicine bottles.

2. A collection of spoons which showed obvious signs of burning.

3. Broken 20-minim syringes and hypodermic needles showing blackening.

4. Metal containers and some small medicine bottles labelled 'Eye Lotion'.

These were handed to Dr J. H. Ryffel, Home Office Analyst, together with material from the autopsy. He reported his findings as follows:

1. Three of the 12oz bottles contained a colourless fluid consisting of morphine hydrochloride 1 grain per oz in chloroform water, making a total of 36 grains of morphine hydrochloride. Another bottle contained morphine with ferric chloride.

2. Four blackened spoons and a blackened metal container all yielded morphine with excess of chloride as also did a dry 1oz bottle labelled 'chloroform'.

3. The broken syringes all yielded morphine on extraction.

He stated that his findings suggested that fluids such as mor-

J

phine in chloroform water had been evaporated down in spoons and metal containers, stored in the small bottles and used for hypodermic injections.

Examination of the pieces of skin and subcutaneous tissue from the autopsy showed morphine to be present, indicating that the dead woman had received an injection at no long period before death. No morphine was recovered from the organs and this would be in keeping with its having been destroyed before death.

Detective Inspector Rutherford reported that the Bonnymans had been living with a Mrs Rosina Madden since eviction from their previous home in August 1941. He found the accommodation to consist of a bedroom containing a double bed, a built-in cupboard and a small table. It was filthy and the bed was badly stained with what appeared to be blood, pus and urine. The floor was littered with papers.

He interviewed Dr William Fenton, who had sent the woman into hospital, and who said that he had gone to the house in answer to a telephone call by a woman at 2.15 p.m. on 12 January. She had told him that Dr Bonnyman wanted him to see his wife urgently, and as he knew something of the background he had thought it wise to ask another doctor to go with him. On arrival at the house they had gone upstairs to the bedroom and in the bed had seen what at first sight appeared to be a bundle of old clothes; on closer examination it had proved to be the woman lying on her left side. In a very weak voice she had asked: 'Who is the gentleman?' When he made himself known she had said: 'It is very kind of you to come and see me.' On examination he found her indescribably dirty with bluish-coloured lips, and after consultation with his colleague decided she should be sent to hospital at once; he told her husband, and the removal was carried out.

Mrs Rosina Madden, the landlady, told Inspector Rutherford that Mrs Bonnyman came to her house in August 1941 and was ill at the time, being carried in by Dr Fenton. She had abscesses at the time but seemed to get over them; she got about the house but never went out. She became ill again in November and used to sit in the kitchen all the time, refusing to eat anything and only occasionally taking jelly. She refused to be touched or have her wounds attended to and only changed her clothes when nobody else was there. She refused to have a doctor when her husband wanted her to do so. The landlady confirmed that about a week before Mrs Bonnyman's death, she was put to bed, but her clothes were not taken off, and that on 12 January she was so bad her husband decided to call a doctor. She also remembered that Mrs Bonnyman had sometimes been quite bright and shortly afterwards depressed and not willing to speak. This had occurred daily. She said she had never realised the room was so dirty and had never seen Mrs Bonnyman treat herself or any sign of chemicals.

Further interviews brought to light that a relation, a Mrs Alice Donovan, had been very surprised when returning to Barking in November to find that the Bonnymans were living in the house. She said that Dr Bonnyman appeared to have let himself go and confirmed what had been said about Mrs Bonnyman's condition. She recalled that on 12 January Mrs Bonnyman had agreed to allow herself to be washed, but when her husband tried to assist she had bitten him but seemed sorry afterwards.

From Inspector Rutherford's inquiries it became quite clear that the past history of the woman must be investigated, and he obtained a statement from a Dr Prasad who had first attended Mrs Bonnyman at the beginning of 1940 at her husband's request. He had found her very ill with a large number of abscesses on the body and limbs which were too deep for him to incise. Some were already discharging pus. Dr Bonnyman had then explained her condition by saying she was stubborn and would not have any attention. Dr Prasad recalled that he had made the significant remark: 'But she is not in a fit condition to give an answer. Her condition is serious and you should have taken action.' Under the impression it was a case of osteomyelitis, he made arrangements for her admission to hospital the same day (13 February 1940).

On admission she had looked ill and worried, and was dirty, very thin and had foul teeth. There was severe ulceration of her right arm and she had volunteered the information that she was addicted to morphine and had been taking 7 grains a day. In hospital the morphine had been slowly reduced and given with hyoscine and she had had her last dose on 23 February. The total given to her was $2\frac{3}{4}$ grains of morphine and $\frac{1}{10}$ grain of hyoscine. From this it was clear that little difficulty was experienced in breaking her of the habit and she was discharged on 16 April 1940, with a weight of 6 stone 11lb, which was still increasing.

Dr Prasad did not see Mrs Bonnyman again until 11 July 1941, when her husband called and told him that the bailiffs were throwing him out of his house and he wanted a certificate to say that his wife was unfit to be moved. He had thereupon visited her and Mrs Bonnyman was carried downstairs to him by her husband in a very emaciated condition, covered with dirt and lice and with abscesses of the scalp. Dr Prasad was quite unable to carry out a proper examination in the presence of the bailiffs but he nevertheless gave the certificate and, feeling worried about the whole thing, called again the next day. At first he got no answer but after a while Dr Bonnyman came round the side of the house and said that his wife was quite all right, and that when he wanted Dr Prasad he would call him.

A Mrs Kate Putnam had visited Mrs Bonnyman in hospital and had struck up a friendship with her which continued until January 1941. Dr Bonnyman then made it quite clear he did not want her to continue to see his wife. However, on 23 April 1941 the Bonnyman house was damaged by bombing during an air raid and Mrs Putnam decided to go and see how her friend was faring. She had to climb into the house through a window and knocked on Mrs Bonnyman's door, in reply to which Mrs Bonnyman said: 'Don't come in.' This did not deter Mrs Putnam who entered and found the woman lying on a mattress on the floor in a filthy state in a filthy room. She said she had been like that for six weeks. Mrs Putnam brought her food and a change of clothes. Dr Bonnyman came in whilst she was there and she said she was taking his wife to her house. He forbade it, to which Mrs Putnam replied: *'You know what will happen to you if anything happens to Betty?'* She then told him that he would be charged with manslaughter, to which he answered: *'That's what I am afraid of.'* After several further visits Mrs Putnam was allowed to move Mrs Bonnyman to her house, and she stayed there for six weeks and improved considerably. She did not want to be washed but Mrs Putnam made her, and she also had a bath with a change of clothing twice a week. She would not allow her hips to be seen but it was obvious they were dirty as the bed clothes were soiled.

Dr Bonnyman slept on a settee in the same room as his wife and was seen to give her injections with a hypodermic needle, which he stated were for anaemia. At the end of the period Mrs Putnam had to go away and the Bonnymans returned to their own house, since when she had seen neither of them.

On 16 January an inquest on Mrs Bonnyman was opened by the late Dr P. B. Skeels, HM Coroner for Metropolitan Essex, who adjourned it after evidence of identification by Dr Bonnyman and medical evidence of the cause of death. Immediately after this Dr Bonnyman approached Inspector Rutherford and said: 'I don't want you to think I let her suffer. She wouldn't let me do much for her but I used to give her soporifics. I couldn't let her suffer.' He then made a second written statement saying that as his wife would not let him give the correct treatment for her wounds, he used to administer phenobarbital sodium and Nembutal as an anodyne and soporific respectively. The only other medicine he tried to give her was some bronchial mixture, of which she would not take a single dose. She wanted morphine but he would not give it to her, and the last she had had, to his knowledge, was in August. He said that she obtained the morphine by purchasing it in dilute form from chemists. Sometimes she took it by mouth and sometimes boiled it down, concentrated it and then took it by injection. His wife wrote with her right hand but was ambidextrous. He explained the needles found in the room as those he had used for injecting his landlady with bee venom for arthritis.

When Inspector Rutherford had visited the Bonnyman room on a second occasion he had taken possession of a full medicine bottle of what, Dr Bonnyman said, was skin lotion. This was shown to contain morphine hydrochloride, and the removal of it (presumably his last supply of the drug) no doubt accounts for what happened next. He telephoned a chemist in East Ham and told him he was bringing a prescription for morphine hydrochloride solution and asked him to have it ready. The police at the time were making enquiries about a man who was obtaining morphine hydrochloride solution from chemists by forged National Health prescriptions, and had arranged to be notified. The chemist consequently informed them, and when Dr Bonnyman arrived he was detained and questioned. He then made a statement in which he admitted that he had been obtaining the drug in this way for some time and explained that both his wife and himself had been drug addicts for several years. He said he had been cured but when he got into financial difficulties in 1940 had again resorted to drugs and, as he had by then been removed from the Dangerous Drugs Register, had purchased morphine in dilute solution and boiled it down, adding bicarbonate of soda to neutralise the acid. He required two 12oz bottles a day and each bottle cost 3s, so that when his finances became very low he commenced to use other doctors' names on National Health prescriptions. Both he and his wife took the drug by hypodermic injection twice a day and both had syringes. Recently his wife had been too ill to load the syringe and he had done it for her up to and including the Saturday before she died.

He was arrested and charged with the manslaughter of his wife on 29 January and in his possession were found two hypodermic needles, one syringe and four 12oz bottles of morphine hydro-chloride solution. When charged, he said he felt ill and asked to see a doctor. He stated that he had been without drugs since 10 p.m. the previous night and must have some, and was given an injection of ½ grain of morphine.

His trial before Mr Justice Humphreys began on 10 March and lasted three days. The case for the prosecution was presented by Mr L. A. Byrne (later Mr Justice Byrne) and Mr Gerald Howard (Treasury Counsel). Mr Linton Thorpe, KC, who appeared for Bonnyman, did not dispute the evidence but based his defence upon the fact that the woman, who was 37 years old and appar-ently in her right mind, had refused all offers of assistance, in-cluding any attempt to wash her or treat her wounds; nor would she allow another doctor to be called. She had declined food and by her own acts had, in his submission, brought about her death. He stressed the fact that whilst there had been many cases of manslaughter by neglect in which the victim was a young child or aged person, there was nothing in law to say that a person of sound mind could be forced against his or her will to have medical aid or be compelled to eat if disinclined to do so.

Dr Bonnyman gave evidence in accordance with his various statements. Under cross-examination he admitted that the only cure for drug addiction was hospital treatment and that his wife should have had it. He stressed her refusal to allow him to treat her or to have another doctor, but agreed that a doctor should have been called, with the reservation that it could not be forced upon a patient if the person did not want it. Several women were called by the defence and gave evidence that Mrs Bonnyman would not have attention, but on cross-examination agreed she should have been removed to hospital.

The prosecution held the view that whereas it accepted that the woman had refused all offers of treatment and had herself assisted in her own death, at the time she was so ill, owing to excessive drug taking and undernourishment, that she was not fit to decide for herself what was good for her. The prosecution also pointed out that not only had Dr Bonnyman supplied the drug to his wife, but the post-mortem findings suggested he had injected the needle into her body. Further, being a medical man, he must have known that the only treatment for a drug addict is the gradual cutting down of the supply *in a hospital* under proper control.

The Judge, in his summing up, dealt at length with the law in respect to manslaughter by neglect. He commented upon the fact that the accused was a doctor and that it was apparent that he was in a position to know what was the matter with his wife and the only possible treatment. He reminded the jury of Dr Prasad's remark to the accused in February 1940 when Mrs Bonnyman was admitted to hospital: 'She is not in a fit condition to give an answer. Her condition is serious and you should have taken action.'

Dr Bonnyman was found guilty of manslaughter and sentenced to 12 months' imprisonment. Before sentence, it was revealed that he had been convicted three times for offences in connection with the Dangerous Drugs Act and had been sentenced to eight months' imprisonment in 1934 for one of these.

Bonnyman appealed on the ground that the main defence had not been put to the jury, viz, that as she was not helpless and was in full possession of her faculties, he had not neglected her but she herself had refused to have proper attention. He submitted that it was not manslaughter if a wife chose to commit suicide in a loathsome manner despite all efforts made by her husband to prevent her. The Court of Criminal Appeal said that the summing-up by Mr Justice Humphreys had been 'faultless' and that it could not interfere. Dr Bonnyman's name was erased from the Medical Register on 2 June 1942 after a full hearing of the facts by the General Medical Council.

Commentary
The case has several points of interest, both legal and medical, for when medical negligence is alleged, the point at issue is rarely

criminal but rather depends upon the interpretation of the phrase 'to the best of my skill and knowledge'. Most cases of medical negligence tried in criminal courts have been associated with alcohol. The question of alleged forgery and of obtaining goods by false pretences was not an issue at the trial, the evidence merely being offered as an explanation of the source of the drugs.

Ethically it has always been regarded as unwise for a doctor to treat his own wife, if only because if she should die he might be suspect, especially if a motive existed for him to want to be rid of her. This does not enter into the case, as there appears to be every evidence that Bonnyman was fond of his wife.

Inspector Rutherford, in his original assessment of the case, summed up the position when he said: 'It is comparable to that of a person who, seeing somebody unknowingly walking towards a precipice, not only does not warn him but at the last moment gives a gentle push.'

11 Science and Crime Detection

SCIENCE, within the context of this discussion, will be used in its broadest sense as dealing with material phenomena and based mainly on observation, experiment and induction. The reason for this choice lies in a desire to avoid limiting the field to the technical subjects such as physics, chemistry, metallurgy and electronics, and to discuss the various disciplines of medicine and include the professional and human relationship between the investigating officers and those who work with them.

All branches of science have made advances during the last seventy years, and as the amount of knowledge has escalated with each decade, so have the methods available for the prevention and detection of crime. Unfortunately, so too has the intelligence, education and adaptability of the criminal. The paradoxical situation, therefore, emerges of a potential race for the application of scientific knowledge between the forces of law enforcement and infringement. Admittedly, the law should have the edge on its opponents by reason of better finance, organisation and opportunities for training, in the same way as the armed FBI operator has the advantage over the gunman. If the dictum of Radzinowicz, that the best form of prevention is detection, be accepted, then one of the matters for our consideration must be whether all branches of science are being employed to the best of advantage, and whether in the face of the present situation too much emphasis is being placed on the rights of the public to have scientific information, and of the danger of misuse of certain processes *vis-à-vis* their value as proper safeguards. As an example, it seems somewhat illogical that a national registry of fingerprints has never been established and that this, one of the only certain methods of identifying a missing person or a case of amnesia, is unavailable unless that person has a criminal record. Surely an argument that every baby (or citizen) should not be identifiable, on the grounds that he might be detected of a crime that he commits later, is quite untenable. Admittedly, there were technical difficulties in the past in preparing and searching such a registry but will it be welcomed with open arms once modern computerisation has overcome them? Yet the stumbling-block has been more socio-political than technical, for in 1937 in answer to a question in which it was stated that there were some 9,000 unidentified persons in hospitals, asylums and other places in Britain, the then Home Secretary said he would not feel justified in considering the question of a national fingerprint registry for the purpose indicated unless he was satisfied that there was a real and genuine desire for such a system. Admittedly Mr Roy Jenkins has more recently expressed views on the subject, yet the omission of the word 'need' is significant and when a decision has to be made, as indeed it must, it will be of interest to see how far it is possible to carry the defence of privacy based on offenders' fear of leaving prints where they do not wish them to be found —to quote the *Police Review*—'Upstairs, downstairs and in my lady's chamber'. Surely there is a point where such an attitude becomes an accessory to the increase in crime instead of a potential deterrent, apart from relieving the grief and distress associated with delay in establishing identity and the enormous expense involved in inadequate identification in other fields. So too, is it beyond the possibilities of the Official Secrets Act to conceal new methods of crime detection, or is it essential to maintain the public morale and its faith in the police by revealing new techniques and even demonstrating them on the television?

Also, it seems strange when methods such as the polygraph, which are used with success in industry and commerce, are neglected in crime detection, and when some private and public enterprises fail to use established preventive methods which could save the police manpower and even physical risk.

These observations have been made as an introduction to the first matter for discussion, which is the part played by science in helping crime. There are numerous examples of the application of scientific and industrial techniques to criminal activities. Perhaps the most outstanding is the thermic lance, which has been described as 'the greatest menace to the security of safes and strongrooms' and by one manufacturer as 'simple, safe, swift and silent'. Strangely enough, it is stated that although the principle of the lance has been applied for over sixty years, its criminal use has only just begun in Britain. Yet when the lance was used for crime, details were described and illustrated in at least one newspaper. As a 'do it yourself' kit, it had certain physical disadvantages from the point of view of portability; but since then an improved model, the flexible thermic cutter, has been duly reported, with the somewhat ingenuous observation that the modern 'model' refutes the conclusion that it will only be of use to criminals aiming for high stakes. The fact that if it had not been given publicity it would not thereby have been precluded from being adopted by an intelligent criminal does not conceal the message of the misuse of science. It may well have been shown on television, for many criminal ideas may have derived from this source, including 'the hypodermic attaché case' in the Kray case and the misuse of domestic gas for homicide. Even surgery has made its contribution, for a skilled safebreaker made a machine based on the principles of a skull trephine to perfect his technique, and added gears in a later model which is in the Black Museum.

Needless to say, an 'A' level standard of chemistry has endless illegal possibilities, perhaps the most lucrative being the 'manufacture' of LSD in the USA and in England as well as 'heroin' in certain parts of the South of France. Countless other examples can be quoted; these simple ones are given to stress the fact that if criminals have adequate scientific training—and such exist— it can be used for evil as well as good. When this situation co- exists with a general lowering of moral and social standards (with, eg, the production and advertising of preparations 'to beat the breathalyser' inspired purely for financial gain) perhaps the time may have come to rethink how science can be more effectively mobilised to assist in law enforcement. In the USA there is a speciality described by Kirk and Bradford as 'criminalistics, which represents much more than laboratory operation. It repre- sents the coalescence of many disciplines to the end-product of science. It is a profession which is rooted in specialised university training and advanced degrees, in professional publications and in scientific and professional associations and affiliations.' Whereas the word 'criminalistics' is not really a proper title, the definition offers a philosophy somewhat similar to that which is the main theme of this paper.

As has already been indicated, *Science* will include all subjects within the various disciplines, and it is proposed to deal with the subsequent discussion under three main headings :

Forensic Science as defined by the work carried out by the forensic science services in this country. This will include applied chemistry, both analytical and physical; physics; bi- ology and other specialities such as metallurgy; questioned documents; ballistics; special applied studies of glass, rubber, explosives, oils and like material.

Forensic Medicine: Pathology, odontology, radiology, immuno- serology and psychiatry.

Criminal Investigation.

The Forensic Sciences

The scope of this section is well exemplified by the contents of Hamish Walls' excellent book entitled *Forensic Science* (1968), which can be usefully supplemented by his presidential address to the British Academy of Forensic Sciences. It will suffice to describe in general the scope of the work of the Forensic Science Laboratories and the services they contribute to the police and public, and in greater detail the advances which have been achieved in certain specialised fields.

Basically, the services cover all aspects of the scientific investigation of crime including larceny, arson, firearms, forgery, but not the physical medical examination of cases which are included in the Offences Against the Person Act. They do, however, examine the biological material collected from such cases and also chemically the human tissues and body fluids from cases of poisoning and offences in which drugs or alcohol are involved. This somewhat surprising arbitrary division will be explained when forensic medicine and pathology are discussed. In the past, members of the staff of the laboratories attended most major incidents, whilst in other cases the material was collected by the investigating officer and conveyed to the laboratory with strict continuity control. However, with the increase in crime and fuller appreciation of the potentialities of scientific examination, in spite of considerable increase in the establishment, the work load made visits to the locus an impossible task except in exceptional cases of difficulty or of major importance. As a result, police officers have been specially trained as 'scenes of crime officers' and are highly experienced in the proper selection, collection, labelling and packing of relevant material. These officers, however, have no academic scientific training, whereas the senior members of the laboratory staff all have university degrees in their special basic subjects and may have higher degrees. Although not often visiting scenes of crime they are always available to advise, either directly or through a police liaison officer who is attached to each laboratory. It should be emphasised that all the scientific staff are independent of the police, are impartial scientists and often show results which help to 'clear' a suspect. The results are given in the form of a report, and this is commonly accepted by the court in lieu of verbal evidence.

The enormous advances which have been made in the technical fields of scientific investigation cannot be overstated. Some of these have resulted from research in other countries but some also have been achieved by workers in the laboratories themselves, and often in their spare time. Although it may be invidious to single out individuals one must here mention the names of Margaret Pereira and Brian Culliford in the field of stains by human tissue fluids, and of Alan Curry in toxicology. The stature of Curry was best exemplified when he was appointed the first Director of the Home Office Forensic Science Research Laboratory at Aldermaston, which has resulted not only in discovering new techniques but in the valuable assessment of apparatus. Amongst some of the recent contributions have been work on the identification of glass fragments and the distribution of carbon monoxide in red blood corpuscles. In close collaboration with the Atomic Energy Commission, research has also been carried out using neutron activation methods, and the importance of advances in the biological field has been underlined in studies on sperm and blood stains.

Not long ago, two cases occurred illustrating the rapidity of advance. In one a man was convicted of murder and subsequently hanged amidst considerable controversy, which could have been settled had it been possible to identify the group of a small trace of blood on his ring. In another case a man was acquitted because although there was a positive chemical test for blood on his jacket, it was too small in quantity either to identify as human or to establish the group. Now it has not only become possible to identify the blood as human but to establish a number of identifying specific characteristics so as to increase the probable source of origin. All this has taken place since 1961. It also illustrates a phenomenon upon which much stress must be placed, the close scientific association which has been established between the workers in the Forensic Science Service and those who are members of an academic University Department of Forensic Medicine. Such liaison with different facilities and material must inevitably lead to further advances. In other specialities similar progress has taken place, and perhaps one of the most exciting forensic achievements has been the identification of cannabis on the skin of the fingers of a woman who was found drowned in the Thames.

Perhaps a significant step in advancing the potentialities of the utilisation of science in the war against crime was the establishment of the Home Office Scientific Advisory Committee—HOSAC. The membership of the committee consists of a number of academic scientists in various subjects including chemistry, physics, telecommunications and pathology (there are two sub-committees in forensic science and equipment, with co-opted members from industry including glass, metallurgy and pharmaceutical chemistry), as well as other academic scientists of distinction. The object is to co-ordinate new techniques and equipment with members of the law enforcement establishments, including forensic science research laboratories and Home Office divisions, and to advise the Home Secretary as to their value and practicability. So far there appears to be evidence that the committee can serve a useful purpose.

Forensic Medicine

Two types of doctor play a most important part in the investigation of crimes against the person:

1. The *Police Surgeon*, who has three functions: firstly, to examine the bodies of persons who are suspected of having died from violence or other forms of unnatural death, and secondly, to examine living persons when there are allegations or suspicions of violence, such as sexual offences and wounding, or when a medical examination is necessary to decide whether they are fit to be detained in custody. A third duty is to collect blood from those who have been detained under the Road Safety Act and to examine those suspected of having infringed the Road Traffic Act.

Unfortunately, cases which fall into the first group are not always seen by specially qualified medical practitioners and hence unnatural deaths are not discovered until examined at the mortuary. Examples of these are too numerous to enumerate. Perhaps the most worrying was one in which a woman was moved to the mortuary as a case of 'natural death' and had scarcely arrived there before a man entered a police station and said he had strangled her. Examination of the body by an expert even before autopsy confirmed his statement and also showed sexual violation, which he admitted.

Until eight years ago there was no qualification in forensic medicine (other than that of the Royal College of Physicians of Edinburgh) but now there is a Diploma of Medical Jurisprudence which should eventually be an indication for selection. In the meantime, until some proper service is established and all cases are examined by those with special training, cases of homicide will be missed or at the best the original scene will have been disturbed.

2. The other experts in forensic medicine are *Forensic Pathologists*, whose position is far from satisfactory. They are in a most ambiguous position, being employed by the coroner who, under the Coroners' Rules (1953), must consult with the Chief of the Police before deciding who shall perform the autopsy on suspected deaths from violence. The autopsy is frequently carried out in a post-mortem room under the administration of the Health Officer who also employs the staff. Many mortuaries are still unsuitably equipped and have no X-ray facilities, whilst in rural areas they may be obsolete in design. With such administrative chaos, it would seem of little use to train 'scenes of crime officers' if the place in which the material is to be collected is so unsatisfactory. However, on an *ad hoc* basis, with the collaboration of the coroner and local pathologists and active support of the police, it has been possible to designate 'special post-mortem rooms' for special cases, whilst the Department of Forensic Medicine at the London Hospital has its own post-mortem room with trained assistants, X-ray and photographic facilities.

The situation in respect of expert forensic pathologists gives

K

cause for much anxiety, especially as they represent the future teachers in the undergraduate field. In all there are only a limited number in practice, for during the past few years no less than three have retired on account of ill-health, and one other has decided to go into academic pathology. In addition, very few have been trained systematically, those university departments which have contributed most being Leeds University, Queen's University, Belfast, and the London Hospital Medical College. The reason for this state of affairs appears to stem from the Spilsbury tradition of individualism, for Sir Bernard never trained any successor and had no one who could get experience, for he also never delegated any of his work. It would seem that a similar position exists now, and whereas no doubt this may produce outstanding personalities, it does little to encourage suitable candidates to take up the speciality. It may also be inherent in the coroners' system as it now exists, whereby each coroner selects the pathologists who work for him, and consequently is loath to sacrifice the substance of the established expert for the shadow of the less experienced person. The late Dr Milne, however, took a keen interest in and trouble with young pathologists who were supervised by their more senior colleagues. It is also somewhat disturbing how few new advances have been made in forensic medicine (pathology) compared with those in forensic science, a fact underlined by the absence of original new material in some textbooks. It may be that, as is suggested later, closer association may stimulate such original research as that done by Cameron on brain lesions following the injection of hypertonic saline into the pregnant uterus (amniocentesis) to produce therapeutic abortion. On the other hand, the lack of advance may result from blind acceptance of textbook information. For example, in the Christie case, it was clear when spermatozoa were recovered from the vaginas of women dead for more than four weeks that the only reason why they had not previously been recovered was that nobody had looked—because the operation was not thought to be worth while or because of too much work load.

In the United States of America, where the organised teaching of forensic medicine in the medical curriculum is limited to malpraxis—with a few notable exceptions such as Boston, Richmond, Baltimore, Los Angeles and Cleveland—the medico-legal expert is the forensic pathologist. His main contact is with autopsies, in which, to be 'boarded', he has to have a systematic training. The broader aspects of legal medicine such as are an essential to the ordinary doctor are not taught, and such examinations as those for rape are commonly left to junior hospital doctors. As a result, it is not uncommon to find that lawyers know more of legal medicine than doctors, and that books and courses are designed to perpetuate such a situation. At first, when working with American lawyers, it can be most irritating to be instructed in one's own subject, but provided you have adequate expertise, the situation will resolve itself. Unlike England and Wales with their forensic science service, the USA (apart from the FBI) relies on police laboratories for a large proportion of its scientific investigation and on local pathologists for autopsies and sometimes for such specialist examinations as those of stains. Unlike the situation here, where the standard is not only high but even, there is a great deal of variation in America. A comparison between the standard of practice of forensic pathology gives the impression that it is higher in this country but that it is also sadly limited in both countries as to numbers. Certainly neither has anything resembling the traditional medico-legal institute on the Continent. Herein there seems to be a clue to the situation.

So far, the traditional applied forms of science—pathology, chemistry, biology and physics, including metallurgy, and firearms—have been considered, but there are others which are newer and have made considerable advances: forensic psychiatry and criminology, which might well contribute to investigation and even prevention. However, it must be emphasised that psychiatry as a whole does not come within this category and has impeded and may well continue to impede justice until, as in the case of all 'growing up' situations, it appreciates its own limitations of knowledge and achieves a true objective approach. This is particularly important in an era when more and more psychiatric cases seem to reside in the security of a prison and more and more dangerous criminals, albeit cases of mental disease, occupy beds with less security in mental hospitals. Perhaps from a scientific point of view a lesson may be learnt from the enthusiasm with which the XYY chromosome was accepted in relation to murder among a highly selected population. Recent research by Sergovich and others (1969) in Ontario demonstrated an incidence of chromosome abnormalities of 1 in 2,159 consecutive births, or 0.4 per cent incidence of XYY type abnormalities among the live male births. Clearly, before any evidence can be properly acceptable in investigation or in evidence (it has already been tried), a great deal more accurate scientific assessment will be required. On the other hand, the fact that hypoglycaemia can cause violence which is often rationally motiveless, seems little appreciated by many psychiatrists who give firm opinions based on personal interview which could mislead the court. The same is equally applicable to some types of violence which to the real expert are clearly sexually motivated, and which, if indicated to the investigating officer or legal adviser, might well be of assistance on interrogation. Criminology might well play a part, and it might be time well spared to study Colin Wilson's *A Casebook of Murder* as affording some insight into the pattern of behaviour in multiple murders.

Criminal Investigation

Nobody can possibly deny that the centrepiece or hub of any investigation is the police officer in charge. Whatever the advances in science, medicine and technology, they can only complement careful, methodical and experienced police investigation, much of which depends upon interrogation. Perhaps it is possible to go further and say that when a doctor or scientist begins to assume the role of a police officer and becomes emotionally involved in a case, there is a potentially dangerous situation in sight. This particularly applies to those whose work is limited to prosecution, and such expressions as 'I got a conviction' are occasionally heard. At the present, certainly in the investigation of murder (with which type of crime, albeit small in numbers, the medico-legal expert who performs autopsies is most likely to become involved), there could be far better use made of both science and medicine than exists at present. Mention has already been made of the built-in advantages the police have over the criminal, including manpower, interpolice co-operation and teamwork, and whilst the law breaker may have the advantage of surprise, technical knowledge and even equipment, his opportunity for research and training is limited. Yet as statistics show, the balance of success still lies against the law, and there is too little margin to allow for any increase in specialised crime. The idea of two heads close together not only being better than one nearby but two or three at a distance is not original, as has been shown by the brilliant success of the police in certain operations recently. A scrutiny of how science and medicine can assist the investigating officer complete a case as rapidly as possible is essential.

Firstly in cases of homicide, early suspicion and confirmation of that suspicion is necessary, and there is no need to stress the fact that if the body is undisturbed there are certain advantages gained, such as accurate photographic records and the continued presence of trace evidence. So too, misinformation as to whether or not a crime has been committed may lead to waste of police time and, even worse, to loss of confidence in the doctor. This, therefore, stresses the importance of close communication between the police and the medico-legal experts—the phrases 'I didn't like to bother you' or 'I know how busy you are' must be expunged from the record. It must also be remembered that the opinion of a doctor, in the eyes of the police, must be believed and that the line of investigation and interrogation may well depend upon the nature and interpretation of the autopsy findings communicated to the police. It might be said that mistakes can always be remedied. This is true to some extent, but recently an eminent American lawyer pointed out that it is the 'charge' that matters, and the subsequent acquittal of an innocent person in a case based on a misconception can never undo the harm that has been done.

From these observations and the information derived from the autopsy, provided that it is competently performed and recorded, the inference must be that the medico-legal specialists must be properly trained and experienced. In addition, certain other observations are essential, including those to estimate the time of death, and supervision of photography, all of which take time, as does the autopsy itself. Now, speed is not necessarily synonymous with efficiency, especially when it is for expediency and has been traditionally accepted. An autopsy can occupy several hours even after primary information is available, but time means adequate manpower and on a fee-for-service basis this means more and smaller slices from the cake. It must be the inevitable conclusion that work involving this responsibility and experience can only be adequately rewarded on a salary basis, in which time is not an issue but efficiency is. Let it be clearly understood that such remuneration, once status has been established, must be on a scale comparable with that of a consultant surgeon having an award *and* include a proper expense allowance and every necessary facility for ancillary investigations. In the past, scientific information has sometimes been sacrificed for financial gain, sometimes under the pretext of 'non-essentiality'. The effect of proper appointments with proper remuneration would certainly lead to better recruitment.

The pattern is beginning to take shape, for the investigating officer should now have easily available medical experts whose ability he knows and with whom he has easy personal contact. It must be obvious that physical proximity is of utmost importance and that the forensic scientists should be included in the picture, for they too must be part of the team. The speed with which information concerning the results of their examinations reaches the investigating officer is just as important, and sometimes more so, than the result of the autopsy. Furthermore, the artificial division of examination of material in a murder case between the pathologist and the forensic scientist is quite unrealistic, on the basis of duplication, and may lead to undesirable competition. Philip Youngman Carter's appendix to *The Investigation of Murder* (1966) advocated establishing specialised teams; experience since has given no reason to modify this opinion.

Summary

The final pattern seems inevitable on logical grounds. The expert medico-legist should, as already outlined, be closely integrated with the forensic scientist, both of whom are available to assist the investigating officer with accurate and rapidly communicated results and advice. In addition, the potential additional assistance of the psychiatrist and criminologist must be increasingly evaluated. In this way, science may well offer greater assistance in investigation *vis-à-vis* evidence. Immediate reactions such as 'impossible', 'impracticable', 'financially unobtainable' will come from certain quarters where *status quo* is the keyword, but not from those true scientists who are prepared to sink individual interests for the benefit of the future establishment of the authority of the law. In anticipation of the obvious criticism that no practical suggestion has been made to deal with the problem of 'multiple' suspects in cases of homicide (and this situation arises in particular in sexually motivated child murders), there is one particular scientific weapon which, although it has been well publicised, has never been acceptable in criminal investigations in this country, but is used for this purpose in the USA and also in the US Services as well as in civil screening. This scientific apparatus is popularly known as the 'lie detector' and its technical name is the Polygraph. Curiously enough its efficiency depends only as to about 5 per cent on the instrument, but as to 95 per cent on the operator, who must be a trained psychologist and interrogator. Its technical success lies in the fact that not only does the examiner note the ordinary reactions to certain questions—as indeed does any investigating officer who has a 'feeling' that the suspect is concealing something—*but* it registers the reactions to certain questions in the form of pulse rate, breathing and blood pressure. These reactions, although not acceptable in court, can be of great value in narrowing down a number of suspects so that the investigation can be concentrated on a small field. Opposition in the past has been based on suggestions that the results would be used in evidence; it must again be stressed that the value of the Polygraph is purely investigational and exclusive. It is rather surprising that another, far less scientific, technique, 'the identikit', has been accepted. In any event this now has to be modified by an artist, but in all cases it depends upon that most dangerous and unreliable person, the 'eye witness'. Philip Youngman Carter in *The Investigation of Murder* stressed the potentialities of the artist, and it would not seem to be impossible to find amateur artists amongst the police and certainly in the photographic departments.

In conclusion, the use of science in the investigation of crime has unlimited possibilities given adequate education, imagination, adaptation, research and finance, and provided that there is proper team work in association with and under the control of the investigating officer who is in charge of the case.

Boddy, R. H. (1969), 'The Flexible Thermic Cutter'. *Police Journal*, XLII, Nov 1969.

Brittain, R. P. (1968), in *Gradwohl's Legal Medicine*, 2nd ed. John Wright, Bristol.

Camps, F. E. (1968), in *Gradwohl's Legal Medicine*, 2nd ed.

Camps, F. E. and Barber, R. (1966). *The Investigation of Murder*. Michael Joseph, London.

Inbau, F. E. and Reid, J. E. (1967). *Criminal Interrogations and Confessions*, 2nd ed. William & Wilkins, Baltimore.

Kirk, P. L. and Bradford, L. W. (1965). *The Crime Laboratory*. Charles C. Thomas, Springfield, Illinois.

Ostler, R. D. (1969). 'The Thermic Lance'. *Police Journal*, XLII, July 1969.

Patterson, A. D. (1960). 'Science and the Courts'. *Journal of the Forensic Science Society*, 1, 1, 5.

Police Review (1970), No 4016. 2 Jan, p 11.
Sergovich, F., Valentine, G. H., Chen, A. T. L., Kinch, A. A. H., Smout, M. S. (1969). *New England Journal of Medicine*, 280, 851-5.
Walls, H. J. (1968). *Forensic Science*. Sweet and Maxwell, London.
Wilson, Colin (1969). *A Casebook of Murder*. Frewin, London.

Appendix   Drugs of Dependence: A Social and Pharmacological Problem

THIS LECTURE, given in 1968, is included as an appendix to the Bonnyman case. It offers a survey of the situation in 1968. Recently, legislation has been introduced in an attempt to tackle this situation, and a summary of it, together with some information as to its effects, is included at the end of the paper.

Drug addiction is a state of periodic or chronic intoxication produced by the repeated consumption of a drug (natural or synthetic). Its characteristics include (1) an overpowering desire or need (compulsion) to continue taking the drug and to obtain it by any means; (2) a tendency to increase the dose; (3) a psychic (psychological), and generally a physical, dependence on the effects of the drug, and (4) detrimental effect on the individual and on society.

Drug habituation is a condition resulting from the repeated consumption of a drug. Its characteristics include (1) a desire (but not a compulsion) to continue taking the drug for the sense of improved well-being which it engenders; (2) little or no tendency to increase the dose; (3) some degree of psychic dependence on the effect of the drug, but absence of physical dependence and hence of an abstinence syndrome; (4) detrimental effects, if any, primarily on the individual (WHO Expert Committee, 1957).

Drug dependence is a state of psychic or physical dependence, or both, on a drug, arising in a person following administration of that drug on a periodic or continuous basis. The characteristics of such a state vary with the agent involved, and these characteristics must always be made clear by designating the particular type of drug dependence in each specific case; for example, drug dependence of the morphine type, of the barbiturate type, or of the amphetamine type (WHO Expert Committee, 1964). A member of the Committee noted that 'the two original terms of addiction and habituation caused some confusion and particularly misuse of the former. Both terms are frequently used interchangeably and often inappropriately . . . The difficulties in terminology became increasingly apparent with the continuous appearance of new agents.'

This paper is concerned with drug dependence, as the World Health Organisation has defined the term. Yet old definitions are often in use while those recommended now are either neglected or quoted out of context. So too, by international agreement and legislation, one substance (cannabis) is controlled by the Dangerous Drugs Act of 1965. Although potentially dangerous in more ways than one, there is little evidence to support any claim against cannabis of the production of any 'dependency' other than a psychological one. On the other hand, there are drugs (LSD, STP, DMT) which are extremely dangerous and, if not causing dependence, may well cause other dangerous effects. To add to the confusion, legislation in England has become more restrictive although it is still based on the idea that drug addiction is a disease, while in the US, which has lived with the same problem for many years and has strictly legislated against it, may become progressively more tolerant.

In the meantime, experts on the subject of addiction spring up overnight from all sorts of different disciplines—journalists, television figures, social scientists, psychologists, psychiatrists, actresses, pop stars, do-gooders, and even doctors—associating drugs, dangerous or otherwise, with everything from the Vietnam war and nuclear disarmament to free love and martyrdom. This confuses the real issue of whether drugs of dependence are really necessary, and, as a corollary, it may be asked how many drugs of any kind are necessary and, if so, why?

In a 1965 Bengue lecture, W. A. R. Thompson suggested that more people died of treatment than disease. We might ask ourselves whether perhaps the medical profession should not examine its own conscience as to the degree of drug dependence, other than that associated with and bred by publicity, for which it is responsible. Figures which will be quoted later may give food for thought. Let it also be quite clear that nothing stated here is intended as criticism of the pharmaceutical agencies, the press, or the radio or television but that it is merely suggested that the time has come to adopt a completely new way of viewing the situation.

It would seem that in order to find a solution to any problem which seems insoluble, it is essential to do a great deal of forgetting and, after that, some re-thinking. This difficult procedure involves the discarding of preconceived ideas.

Problems associated with drug dependency (addiction) have been, and still are, arbitrarily divided into those associated with the hard and the soft drugs. Addiction to narcotics is not a new phenomenon in the USA and Canada, but apart from therapeutic addiction, it is relatively new in its present form in this country. The 'soft drug' problem is, as an overt situation, something which has not been properly appreciated until recently by the medical profession. There is also the real problem associated with alcoholism which is not new either, but which, even in the present politico-public hysterical reaction to drug addiction, is hardly mentioned outside an outcry concerning death and injury in road accidents due to drinking. Alcohol and drugs exert a pharmacological action on the human organism which is physical and psychological, produces behavioural changes, and can lead to dependence.

What is the justification for assuming that all addicts have developed the disease for the same reason? There may in fact be different reasons for addiction or dependence on drugs and alcohol, and just as different bacteria respond to different antibiotics, so individual addicts may by reason of variation in cause respond to different treatment. At some points, medical treatment for addicts is indicated (as in septicemia or hepatic failure, for instance), though psychiatric intervention seems to be the most usual course. It would seem that as a result of the idea that all alcoholics are a nuisance and all addicts are the same, the tolerance of psychiatrists in accepting such cases and thereby relieving practitioners of an unwelcome responsibility has resulted in the whole problem of the disease of drug and alcohol dependence being thrust into the care of psychiatry.

As an onlooker, from observations made while performing autopsies in mental hospitals, the laboratory facilities did not appear to be adequate either in staff or equipment and certainly few were comparable with those in a general hospital. Such a situation could not possibly deal with the monitoring of patients receiving drugs of the sedative types—and there are few psychiatric cases that are not receiving such drugs, even for sleeping, every day. The dangers of barbiturate intoxication and dependency must be more generally recognised.

At a recent two-day symposium on drug addiction, Connell stated that the two main problems confronting those who were about to be put in charge of the new centres for addicts were, first, to know whether the person was an addict or merely claimed to be one and, second, to determine the amount of drug the addict needed to prevent withdrawal symptoms and to maintain him in equilibrium, as opposed to how much he might want in order to sell the surplus. With respect to heroin, there is very little use in looking to the United States or Canada for assistance, for the position of these countries is entirely different. There the posses-

sion of heroin is completely illegal, even for the medical profession. All supplies of heroin to addicts are therefore derived
from illegal sources. The result is that the heroin addict does not
really know what the real effects of the drug are and, apart from
the placebo effect, probably gets more 'kick' from the other
drugs which he takes in conjunction with it, such as glutethimide,
barbiturates, and the like, boosted by the pleasure of the injection. It would be of particular interest from an epidemiological
point of view if some typology of drug users could be found.
This might prove in the end to be, at least in part, genetic.

The origin of 'casual' addiction to the hard drugs in this
country dates back to 1958 (Bewley, 1966). Prior to this there
were a certain number of therapeutic addicts who were known
to the Home Office, either because of unofficial communication
by the patient's own doctor or from inspection of the records of
chemists' sales which revealed an excessive amount of the drug
for a particular patient. As an example of therapeutic addiction,
there is the case of Mrs Morell whose record of prescriptions
showed an escalating quantity of hard drugs over the period
following her fractured femur until her death. Unfortunately she
was cremated so it was impossible to examine the body or perform any toxicology. As a more classical example of 'morphine'
addiction, there is the case of Mrs Bonnyman who, unlike Mrs
Morell, died of infection and abscess formation at the sites of
injection. The source of her supply was from Liq. Morph. which
was concentrated by boiling by her medically qualified husband
who was also an addict.

In 1961, the first Brain Committee report stated that there was
no real problem in relation to hard drug addiction, although it
noted that cases of therapeutic addiction were recognised. However, even then (although unknown to the Brain Committee)
there were a number of medical practitioners who were 'treating'
addicts with maintenance doses which were altered from time to
time. Although there is no reason to believe that the statements
of these doctors were incorrect, on the basis of the behaviour of

those who were dependent upon a drug, tolerance should have developed and required progressive dosage increase. In addition, a more worrying aspect appeared when it was found that certain of these doctors were also prescribing cocaine. The number of addicts was increasing and the age of users was decreasing.

The Brain Committee was reconvened in 1964 and reported its conclusions and recommendations (1965), which are the basis of the legislation which has now been implemented and which will allow only licensed doctors to supply heroin and cocaine to addicts. Even before implementation it is becoming clear that whereas most doctors have a high standard of integrity—apart from a dislike of treating 'junkies'—there is a small minority who have been prescribing the drugs far in excess of estimated requirement and sometimes for a fee. Then the almost inevitable surplus was sold to 'friends' who therefore supported the market, and also the addict, to the extent of £1 per grain. Clearly, the main source of the drug was the prescriptions of these doctors. Not only was this a danger, but the same doctors were also supplying other drugs including methedrine, and there will be nothing to prevent their doing so even after the new regulations are implemented. There must, therefore, be a genuine risk that some addicts will agree to substituting methadone or morphia for heroin and methedrine for cocaine.

The Cause of Death of Heroin Users

Although a great deal has been omitted from the discussion on dependence on the hard drugs, this has been deliberate as the subject has been discussed ad nauseam during the last few years. Furthermore, it was not my intention to devote much space to a problem which is now outside the field of clinical medicine and which, according to the success or failure of the new legislation, will become self-limiting or criminological. For a considerable time, the situation with regard to the cause of death of addicts was untidy, unsatisfactory, and usually incorrect. Accordingly a project was submitted to the Home Office which in its turn handed it over to the Ministry of Health. Basically it was simplicity itself, taking the form of a request to have access to material from all addicts who died. This in no way interfered with the pathologist other than to make him exert himself to collect the material. This suggestion was quite acceptable to both the Home Office and to the Ministry of Health and the investigation has, in fact, justified the enormous amount of chemical analysis which it has entailed.

The deaths of addicts have been well reviewed in papers by Bewley (1966) and James (1967) but their observations were based on second-hand information. Clearly all addicts using the intravenous or sub-cutaneous route for injection are running a severe risk from infection. In fact, it has been surprising how few deaths are from this cause.

Multiple drug habits will probably be even more common in the future. Whereas some drug users have died of an overdose after prior withdrawal, most have died from the combined effects of more than one drug. These may include heroin, cocaine, barbiturates, amphetamines, and even alcohol. Many cases who are accepted as having died from withdrawal of heroin more probably died of barbiturate withdrawal.

Stimulants

These drugs (benzedrine, methedrine, dexedrine, and Drinamyl), introduced in 1930, have been subject to epidemic misuse not only in this country but also in Japan where in the Kurume episode over 1 per cent of the total population and 5 per cent between the ages of 16 and 25 were involved. It was estimated that by 1954 there were half a million regular users in Japan and that half of these were addicted. After 1956 there were an increasing number of papers published concerning the situation. Apart from the outstanding publications by Connell (1958; 1962) on the subject, others of considerable interest have been published stressing the dangers of the drug, notably those of Kiloh and Brandon (1962) who stated that 'the amphetamines in general are prescribed readily and light-heartedly', a masterpiece of understatement: Out of 119,208 scripts in May 1960 (Newcastle-upon-Tyne), 4,052 were for amphetamine preparations (3·4 per cent), while the amount of amphetamines prescribed at two other hospitals was 223,500 tablets in May and 176,000 tablets in November, 55 per cent dispensed as Drinamyl. Oswald and Thacore (1963) writing on amphetamine and phenmetrazine (Preludin) addiction gave the price of Drinamyl tablets on the 'black market' as £1 for 24 in London and £1 for 25 in Edinburgh. Wilson (1964) defined 'ill advised medications' as 'the treatment of patients by drugs without sufficient justifiable indication for their use'. In fact, it is now generally accepted that the drug is of little value for 'slimming' and has no place in psychiatric treatment, the only possible use being for the 'tired housewife' under proper supervision—if this is possible! According to Goldberg the amphetamines were advertised in the Swedish newspapers as 'two pills are better than a month's vacation'.

The situation in Sweden was similar to that in Japan. Figure 6 shows the sales of amphetamine in Sweden from 1938-43 and also shows the effects of warnings to the medical profession. During this period, it was estimated that there were about 200,000 users in Sweden.

The next phase commenced in 1956-7 and culminated in 1958-9. The abuse of the drug spread to a younger age group, often with a criminal background, and abuse of stimulant drugs became a fashion.

In 1958, methylphenidate (Ritalin) and phenmetrazine (mainly as Preludin) were in use and, as a result of the increasing number of cases, in 1959 these two drugs were designated as narcotic drugs under the Swedish Narcotics Drugs Act. In 1960 a circular of warning was sent to the medical profession naming the most abused drugs and this resulted in a reduction from 1960 to 1961 in narcotic prescriptions by 11 per cent and stimulant drugs by 29 per cent.

The troubles in Sweden have been repeated in the British Isles,

L*

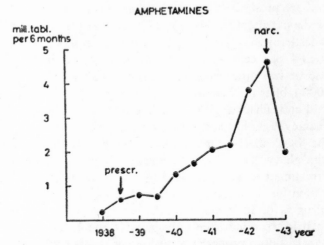

Fig 6   Sales of amphetamines in Swedish pharmacies, 1938-43
1939—sale of amphetamines by prescription only
1943—warning issued to the medical profession by the
National Medical Board on risks of use and abuse
of stimulants

and a wave of amphetamine abuse has spread through the country
particularly among young adults and teenagers. Some amphetamines have come from over-prescription but more from ware-
house- and shop-breaking. The use pattern takes two forms: (1)
continuous daily consumption and (2) weekend excesses, some
teenagers taking as much as 2,000-3,000mg a day.

There can be no doubt that amphetamine is a drug of addiction, that it can produce dangerous effects and that its demand
has encouraged criminal activities.

Sedatives and Hypnotics

Bromide intoxication, which is only now seen in association with
the treatment of some cases of epilepsy, or the indiscriminate use
of proprietary remedies, takes the form of impairment of memory,
drowsiness, emotional instability, and irritability, while delirium,
delusions, and mania may occur in severe cases. In most cases

which exhibit intoxication, the serum bromide level exceeds 20 meq/liter.

Whereas acute toxicity is manifested by respiratory failure, chronic misuse of chloral hydrate can produce tolerance and physical dependence with symptoms similar to delirium tremens on sudden withdrawal. Ethchlorynol (Placidyl) is a tertiary acetylenic alcohol with a marked hypnotic action. It can cause exaggerated reaction when taken with alcohol. Habituation with tolerance may develop in patients receiving 1·5g per day. Paraldehyde in acute overdosage will produce respiratory depression. Again chronic overdosage produces similar effects to barbiturate intoxication, while habituation can occur and withdrawal symptoms resemble delirium tremens.

Ethinamate (Valmid) closely resembles quinalbarbitone in its action; it is a carbamic acid ester of an alicyclic alcohol. Dependence occurs with withdrawal symptoms comparable with those of the barbiturates. Piperidinedione derivatives (glutethimide—Doriden, methyprylon—Noludar) closely resemble quinalbarbitone in effect but have one feature which can be dangerous if misused by repeat doses (Doriden in particular is taken by some heroin addicts): They are secreted fairly slowly in the bile and re-absorbed from the intestine. Tolerance, habituation, and dependency have occurred with withdrawal symptoms characterised by nausea, insomnia, confusion, and generalised convulsions.

The barbiturates, when first introduced, were actively and widely condemned as dangerous. For a period there was considerable controversy within the medical profession. No doubt the opponents are now to some extent justified for these drugs represent one of the major problems of therapeutics and the full extent of their side effects may still not be fully recognised. As a matter of comment, the thalidomide experience arose as a direct result of a misplaced hope that a drug had been found to replace the barbiturates, a hope which was publicised to the extent of advertising Distaval as safe. On the basis of therapeutic and animal trials it did appear to be so, but the false safety was to

L

some extent due to poor absorption and the unusual feature of being teratogenic only in the first 40 days of pregnancy.

It is clear that the hypnotic and sedative drugs have been treated with too little respect both by the public and medical profession. Many of them show a sorry history of lack of appreciation of their pharmacological action, their toxic effects, and their lethal potentiality. All in all there is a sad story of failure in the past to appreciate that many, if not all, have all the attributes of drugs of dependence. In fact, the Brain Committee with its limited terms of reference indicted a small number of doctors of the offence of over-prescribing heroin, but had these terms been wider and its investigations more extensive, it might equally well have criticised many members of the medical profession for doing the same with barbiturates. Statistical information, derived from 'The Report on the Census of Production for 1958, Part 29, Pharmaceutical Preparations' (HMSO 1962) concerning the sales and prescribing of barbiturates, makes this clear (see Table 1).

TABLE 1

Sale of Drugs (UK)

	1954 tablets ($\times 1000$)	1958 tablets ($\times 1000$)
Acetylsalicylic acid (aspirin)	2,777	2,539
Aspirin compounds	1,923	3,249
Barbiturates	805	855

Comparable figures are given by the *American Druggist* for the years 1963-7 (Tables 2 and 3). One feature of these figures is that whereas the figures for barbiturates appear to have become stationary in 1966-7, those for tranquilisers have shown a steady increase. Statistical information on deaths from poisoning during the ten years 1955-65 in England and Wales are shown in Table 4 (in accidental deaths barbiturates are shown separately; in the case of suicidal deaths, they are classified within analgesics and soporifics).

TABLE 2

Major Ingredients Used in Prescriptions (United States)

	1963	1964	1965	1966
Tranquillising drugs	85,113,000	96,013,000	97,374,000	102,811,000
Barbiturates	79,552,000	82,064,000	84,764,000	81,810,000
Narcotics	36,180,000	33,440,000	34,641,000	33,375,000

TABLE 3

Breakdown of Prescriptions
(United States)

	1963	1964	1965	1966	1967
Sedatives tranquillisers	112,990,000	122,524,000	123,328,800	124,341,000	130,931,000
Analgesics (internal)	51,008,000	52,330,000	55,447,000	61,868,000	68,223,000
Stimulants	22,909,000	20,486,000	23,958,000	23,196,000	26,340,000

TABLE 4
Deaths in England and Wales from Poisoning

	I Accidental Barbiturates Aspirin	II Suicide Analgesic and Soporifics	III Suicide Crude Death Rates Per Million Analgesics and Soporifics	IV Accidental Crude Death Rate Barbiturates
1955	192 (31)	595	13	4
1956	223 (39)	702	16	5
1957	208 (44)	695	15	5
1958	205 (42)	675	17	5
1959	232 (43)	778	17	5
1960	293 (65)	839	18	6
1961	303 (67)	1,019	22	7
1962	393 (64)	1,305	28	8
1963	482 (60)	1,670	36	10
1964	516 (57)	1,798	38	11
1965	525 (36)	1,803	38	11

The incidence of death from barbiturate poisoning among cases examined in my department, 1965-8, is shown in Table 5; due to the analytical facilities available in the department, it has been possible to break these cases down into the types of barbiturates involved (Table 6).

TABLE 5
Verdicts of Deaths Due to Barbiturate Poisoning, 1965-8

	1965		1966		1967		1968		
	M	F	M	F	M	F	M	F	Total
Accident	5	9	9	5	9	8	5	5	55
Suicide	61	66	37	59	46	59	8	13	349

TABLE 6
Type of Barbiturates Department of Forensic Medicine (LHMC)

	1965		1966		1967		1968		
	M	F	M	F	M	F	M	F	Total
Fast	8	9	10	6	13	8	3	1	58
Intermediate	61	58	55	39	58	54	18	12	355
Slow	6	2	3	3	7	5	1	0	27

The conditions for which these drugs are prescribed are extremely relevant and can be summarised briefly as (1) for sedation and (2) for insomnia. The long-acting barbiturate (sodium barbitone) was used in the past for night sedation and phenobarbitone for control of epilepsy, for sedation, and for night sedation. Clearly the disadvantages of such drugs lay in the fact that all or part of each dose had to be eliminated by excretion, which could lead to retention and intoxication, while in the case of phenobarbitone abrupt discontinuation might well cause withdrawal effects, including epileptiform convulsions. This aspect of barbiturate prescribing has been insufficiently recognised. So, too, it is now becoming realised that many other drugs, including tranquilisers, can produce serious withdrawal effects, thereby complicating an already complicated clinical picture—especially when more than one drug is prescribed.

Dependence upon the barbiturates has certain similarities to dependence upon drugs of the morphine group. There is, however, a somewhat different picture during both intoxication and withdrawal. Repeated administration leads to increased psychic dependence and the patient develops tolerance within as little as seven days; following withdrawal of the drug, tolerance is rapidly lost and some individuals may be more sensitive to readministration.

Chronic use can cause ataxia, accident proneness, impairment of mental ability, and confusional instability. According to Isbell (1951), the clinical manifestations of chronic barbiturism are similar to those of alcoholism. (I have had under my care a doctor using barbiturates who was accused of being 'drunk' when visiting his patients.)

The barbiturate abstinence syndrome begins within 24 hours after cessation of the drug, reaches its peak intensity in two or three days and subsides slowly. Unlike nalorphine with morphine, no drug will precipitate it. It consists of anxiety, involuntary twitching of muscles, tremors of the hands and fingers, progressive weakness, dizziness, distortion of visual perception, nausea, vomiting, loss of weight, insomnia, postural hypotension, convulsions of the grand mal type, and a delirium like that seen in alcoholism. Convulsions and delirium do not occur at the same time. Psychotic episodes may take the form of paranoid reactions and reactions which resemble schizophrenia with delusions and hallucinations; sometimes there is a withdrawn semi-stuporous state with disorganised panic.

The danger to society is related to the individual's preoccupation with drug taking and to the persistence of the effects of the drugs on motor functioning, emotional stability, and interpersonal relationships. By analogy, *all* agents which produce barbiturate-like sedation could produce psychic dependence (because of relief of anxiety) as well as physical dependence, once sufficient concentration in the body has been attained. This possibility is a fact with many sedative agents such as glutethimide, methyprylon, meprobamate, chlordiazepoxide, bromisoval, chloral hydrate and paraldehyde.

There is no evidence that the mechanism of physical dependence will start with the first dose, as in morphine. Nor is there evidence that physical dependence develops to an appreciable degree with *continued* therapeutic doses adequate to produce sedation. The daily dosage must be increased above the usual therapeutic level before abstinence symptoms occur on abrupt withdrawal. Whereas psychic dependence may occur with therapeutic doses, such dosage can be discontinued without serious subjective disturbance; but factors that may lead to increasing consumption and overt physical dependence, such as incomplete relief of emotional problems and tension and impairment of judgement, will often—probably nearly always—lead to larger doses unless adequately controlled. Herein lies the rub, for who does control the dose at home once it is prescribed? And what happens when the patient asks for more? There is another very important factor that is most commonly overlooked, for slight manifestations of some of the above symptoms will also occur —changes in the patient are not easy to detect.

The Hallucinogens

One of the features of the history of drug dependence, or perhaps it would be more accurate to say the drugs upon which people are now becoming dependent, is the fact that many of them date back thousands of years and were used as part of religious ceremonies and other feasts. Yet there seems to have been little evidence of gross social misuse.

The two major natural hallucinogenic drugs are derived from the peyote cactus and a mushroom of the genus *Psilocybe*. The important alkaloids are mescaline and psilocybin, both of which produce hallucinations (some of which are visual), loss of time sense, and, in toxic doses, atropine-like symptoms and death. These drugs now are used on certain occasions by native Indians in the United States without obvious anti-social or addictive effects.

In connection with 'traditional' drugs, Clark (1940) in his book on pharmacology stated two rules in regard to drugs of addiction. (1) When a race is introduced to a powerful drug to which it is not accustomed the results are usually disastrous. Interpreted in the modern terminology of epidemiology, the introduction of an infective organism into a nonimmune population produces a similar effect. This may well be true if the population is receptive or suggestible and may well be one explanation for the recent outbreaks of drug addiction of epidemic proportions. (2) Certain races are inclined to drug abuse: Egypt went through phases of hashish, cocaine, and heroin use. Between 1920 and 1930 the number of heroin addicts is said to have risen to 500,000 out of a total population of 14 million. This—and it may be a lesson—was reduced by vigorous restrictive measures, and during 1929-34, 31,000 drug traffickers and addicts were convicted. On the other hand, Clark cites the Japanese as an example of a race with no addictive tendencies, which is clearly erroneous in view of the serious contemporary outbreak of amphetamine dependence.

It was not until the synthesis of d'lysergic acid diethylamide (LSD-25) at Sandoz that the hallucinogens began to play an important part in the problems of drug abuse. There is controversy about the properties of LSD with respect to physical addiction and withdrawal; recently the possibility of teratogenic properties has been raised. A high degree of tolerance to LSD and to psilocybin develops rapidly and disappears rapidly. Tolerance to mescaline develops slowly; there is cross tolerance among all three drugs. A minority of users develop psychic dependence, but there is no evidence of physical dependence. The main risks of the drugs lie in impairment of judgement leading to accidents and depression leading to suicide.

Discussion

'Fools and wise men are equally harmless. Dangerous are those who are half foolish and half wise and see only half of everything'

As mentioned early in this paper, the whole problem of drug dependence requires re-thinking and this is underlined by the difficulties experienced by the WHO Committee in defining dependence, saying 'the difficulties in terminology become increasingly apparent with the appearance of new agents'. It could also be added 'with increasing experience with the old'. The information available for study can be divided under different headings.

Most of the 'natural' (as opposed to 'manufactured') drugs have been known to be pharmacologically potent for centuries. For the most part they were used on religious and festive occasions. No doubt they were overused from time to time. Certainly this applied to alcohol. But there is little evidence of continuous abuse except, possibly, when civilisation was deteriorating.

Robert Merton has said: 'In strictly economic terms there is no relevant difference between the provision of licit and of illicit goods and services.' So long as there is a market which pays for narcotics, organised crime will furnish the supply; heroin pays and it is not those who take the profits who are arrested. The same applies to prostitution and gambling. It has been said that the number of heroin addicts in Britain is about the same as in

British Columbia—and illicit heroin pays there.

The 'soft' drugs present a somewhat different problem, for here we have an acute epidemic which is only in part due to medical sources of supply. Paradoxically, crime has been assisted and not deterred by the press, for the prosecution of popular 'idols' has been accompanied by publicity—and children are great imitators. Perhaps the crest of the wave of drug use has passed, but it must be clear that there will be wreckage left behind in those with mental changes or those who have been introduced to violence through the use of the drugs. This situation may be part of a general discontent in the same way as other forms of irresponsibility are, but there are parallel situations in over-affluent and over-civilised Sweden and Japan. It would seem to go deeper, and there may well be other factors, including organised revolt in a permissive population which has lost convention and self-discipline.

Yet another form of drug dependence probably involves more people, is more dangerous, and less recognised. Before the escalation of narcotic addiction there were 'therapeutic' addicts. These were few in number and they were treated sympathetically; they were commonly in the medical and nursing professions. There are still 'therapeutic' addicts—but how many it is impossible to guess, except from the amount of barbiturates and tranquillising drugs manufactured and sold. These drug-dependent people probably do not know they are dependent, nor do the doctors who have made them addicted realise it. They do not realise that some of the symptoms to which treatment is directed are themselves due to drug dependency.

One of the most important factors in drug abuse is the source of supply. The control of this factor has been the basis of almost all measures in the past. The stated policy has been to deal severely with the distributor whose motive is financial gain and leniently and humanely with the addict who is a sick person. This is an over-simplification of the matter because some of the addicts are also distributors in order to obtain money to purchase further

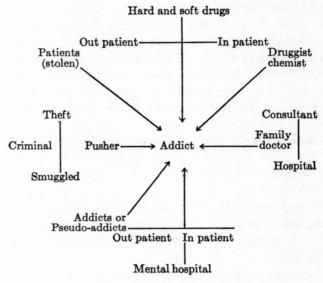

Fig 7 Drugs: sources of supply

supplies, while some of the distributors do not appreciate that they are responsible for the supplies of drugs.

As demonstrated in Figure 7, a large part of the drugs destined for misuse comes from the medical profession through indiscriminate over-prescribing. Due to the impossibility of direct supervision in the home, there are many unrecognised cases of drug intoxication and withdrawal syndromes. The public is demanding more and more drugs of the hypnotic and sedative group. Often the drug is prescribed because the patient wants it and not because he needs it. There is only one answer to this: education of the medical profession at both undergraduate and postgraduate levels, and education of the public by appropriate publicity—which should be indirect rather than direct. Finally, every doctor should remember that 'Drugs cure the sick but make the healthy ill.'

REFERENCES

Bewley, T. Recent modifications in the structure of toxicomania in the United Kingdom. *U.N. Bulletin on Narcotics* 18: 4, 1966.

Clark, A. J. *Applied Pharmacology*, 7th ed. London: J. & A. Churchill, 1940.

Connell, P. H. *Maudsley Monograph No 5: The Amphetamines*, 1958; and The amphetamines, 1 and 2. *Medical World* 96: 18, 106, 1962.

Drug Addiction: First Report of the Interdepartmental Committee, 1961; and *Drug Addiction: Second Report of the Interdepartmental Committee*, 1965. London: Her Majesty's Stationery Office.

James, I. P. *Brit. J. Addict.* 62: 391, 1967.

Kiloh, L. G. and Brandon, S. Habituation and addiction to amphetamines. *Brit Med J* 2: 40, 1962.

Oswald, I. and Thacore, V. R. Amphetamine and phenmetrazine addiction —Physiological abnormalities in the abstinence syndrome. *Brit Med J* 3: 427, 1963.

Recent Legislation and an Appraisal of its Effects

1967: Dangerous Drugs Act (1967). This resulted from the second report of the Brain Committee, extending the power to make regulations under the Dangerous Drugs Act, and (i) requires medical practitioners to notify drug addicts, (ii) prohibits medical practitioners from providing specific drugs to addicts except under licence, and (iii) regulates the safe custody of drugs.

1969: Regulation (S1 1968-136). The Dangerous Drugs (Notification of Addicts) Regulation.

1. Any medical practitioner who attends a person who he considers, or has reasonable grounds to suspect, is addicted to any drug, shall within seven days of the attendance furnish in writing to the Chief Medical Officer of the Home Office such of the following particulars as are known to him:

Name; address; sex; date of birth; National Health Service number; the date of attendance and the name of the drug or drugs concerned.

2. Definition: a person shall be regarded as addicted only if, as the result of repeated administration, he has become dependent upon the drug and has an overpowering desire for the administration to be continued.

3. Exceptions. (i) It is not necessary to comply if the doctor is satisfied that the administration is required to relieve pain from organic disease or injury. (ii) If certain other persons have notified the case.

4. Penalty. The Home Secretary can make a directive prohibiting the doctor from prescribing drugs.

If the Home Secretary considers there is a case for making a directive, he can refer the matter to a tribunal, which will consider the case and report to him. If a directive is made, the doctor must be informed and may make written representation; and if such representation is received, the Home Secretary must refer it to an advisory board, whose advice he will consider in deciding whether or not to make a directive.

Supply to Addicts: a doctor shall not supply, administer or authorise the supply to an addict other than for relief of pain due to organic disease, or under authority and condition of licence, or if authorised by another practitioner with a licence. This applies to cocaine and diamorphine.

Safe custody of drugs (Section 4) emphasised regulations to be made for safe custody. The Drugs (Prevention of Misuse) Act 1967 makes possession of various drugs illegal unless prescribed. These include lysergide and mescaline.

The Misuse of Drugs Act 1971 is only partially in effect (April 1973). The Statutory Instrument allowing establishment of the Committee and consequent administrative detail has been published but no date for full implementation has been announced. The Misuse of Drugs Act will replace the Dangerous Drugs Act and the Drugs (Prevention of Misuse) Act 1967.

The effect of the new legislation has been to reduce the overall use of heroin by addicts but there has been replacement by methadone, often administered by intravenous injection. There has also been an increase in the use of other drugs including barbiturates and methaqualone (as Mandrax) and other tranquillisers and hypnotics, some being taken by injection. There seems to have been some reduction in amphetamine misuse, contributed to by voluntary reduction in prescribing by groups of medical practitioners quite apart from the legal measures restricting possession to those for whom the drug is prescribed. One effect has been to recognise that indiscriminate prescribing does occur and that loopholes existed whereby a medical practitioner could misuse his right to prescribe.

Notes and Acknowledgements

1 *Crime in Hunter's Time* was a Hunterian Oration delivered to the Hunterian Society.

2 *More about Jack the Ripper* is reprinted from the *London Hospital Gazette*, April 1966.

3 *Motives for Murder* is adapted from a lecture given at the Galveston University Medical School, Texas, in February 1959.

4 *The Colchester Taxi Cab Murder* was read at a meeting of the Medico-Legal Society on 25 November 1948.

5 *The Mummy of Rhyl* is reprinted from *Medicine, Science and the Law*, October 1961.

6 *Unexpected Death* is reprinted from *Transactions of the Medical Society, London*.

7 *Attempted Murder by Electrocution* is reprinted from *The Medical Journal of the South-West*, July 1956.

8 *Carbon Monoxide Poisoning* was read at a meeting of the Medico-Legal Society on 27 April 1950.

9 *Alleged Murder by Household Gas*.

10 *The Bonnyman Case* is reprinted from *The South African Medical Journal*, 27 December 1952.

11 *Science and Crime Detection* was the Peter Le Neve Foster Lecture delivered to the Royal Society of Arts on 28 January 1970.

Appendix : Drugs of Dependence was the John Priestman Memorial Lecture delivered at the University of Aston on 7 May 1968.

I should like, once again, to express my gratitude to the following persons and organisations for their help in the preparation of certain papers. (The numbers in brackets refer to individual papers, as above; ranks, positions, etc, are those which applied when the papers were written.)

(2) R. I. Milne, HM Coroner for Greater London (Inner North); A. J. Hardy of the Department of Forensic Medicine at The London Hospital Museum. (4) Captain Peel, Chief Constable of Essex; Detective Superintendent G. H. Totterdell and the officers under his command. (7) L. H. Jesty of the London Electricity Board. (8) The various Coroners who investigated the cases quoted; F. C. Smith, FCS. (9) The Director of Public Prosecutions; Detective Superintendent Millington and Detective Inspector O'Shea; Mr Prigg and his colleagues in the North Thames Gas Board. (10) Dr Percy Skeels, Coroner for Metropolitan Essex; Lieutenant Colonel Rutherford, Chief Constable of Oxfordshire.

My special thanks go to E. Gerald Evans, MRCS, LRCP, for allowing me to reprint his paper on the pathological investigation in the 'Mummy of Rhyl case'.

The publishers would like to thank Dr Ann E. Camps, Dr J. Malcolm Cameron, Reader in Forensic Medicine at The London Hospital Medical College, Miss Jean Reynolds, Public Relations Officer at The London Hospital, and Jonathan Goodman for their help in preparing this collection following the death of Professor Camps.